HENRY LAWSON'S
✤ BUSH BALLADS ✤

Selected Poems and Prose by Henry Lawson   Paintings by Dorothy Gauvin

HENRY LAWSON'S
✦ BUSH BALLADS ✦

Selected Poems and Prose by Henry Lawson　　　　　*Paintings by Dorothy Gauvin*

ANGUS
& ROBERTSON

An imprint of HarperCollins*Publishers*

AN ANGUS & ROBERTSON BOOK
An imprint of HarperCollinsPublishers

First published in Australia in 1991 by
CollinsAngus&Robertson Publishers Pty Limited (ACN 009 913 517)
A division of HarperCollinsPublishers (Australia) Pty Limited
4 Eden Park, 31 Waterloo Road, North Ryde, NSW 2113, Australia

William Collins Publishers Ltd
31 View Road, Glenfield, Auckland 10, New Zealand

HarperCollinsPublishers Limited
77–85 Fulham Palace Road, London W6 8JB, United Kingdom

National Library of Australia
Cataloguing-in-Publication data:

Lawson, Henry, 1867–1922.
  Bush ballads.
  Includes index.
  ISBN 0 207 17116 5.
  I. Gauvin, Dorothy. II. Title.
A821.2.
Cover It'll Rain *by Dorothy Gauvin, 1978*
Typeset in 11/12pt New Baskerville
Printed in Hong Kong
Dorothy Gauvin,
P.O. Box 601,
Cairns, QLD 4870
Telephone: (070) 54 3615
5 4 3 2 1
95 94 93 92 91

CONTENTS

HENRY LAWSON

✤

HENRY LAWSON

Henry Lawson's birth in a tent on the goldfields at Grenfell, New South Wales, in 1867 set the stage for his tumultuous life. The son of Peter Lawson, a gold miner, building contractor and itinerant worker and Louisa Lawson, suffragette and newspaper proprietor, he has become a symbol of an Australian nationalism emerging during his most productive literary years.

Lawson spent his earliest years on the goldfields but his parents settled on their selection at Pipeclay in 1873. By this time there were three children and Peter's search for work left the young family often alone. Henry became both company and support for his mother and bore more knowledge than the younger children of his parents' marital difficulties. The isolation and harshness of the bush would later become a major theme in his work.

Louisa fought to have a school established and Henry was nine years old by the time he started at Eurunderee Public School. In the same year, 1876, he became slightly deaf after an illness. His hearing deteriorated when he was 14 and he was left with a major and incurable hearing loss. He eventually sought treatment at the Victorian Eye and Ear Hospital in 1887 but with no success.

His schooling—such as it was—finished in 1880 and he worked with his father on local building jobs, sometimes travelling as far as the Blue Mountains. He left his life in the bush in 1883 to live with his mother in Sydney and was an apprentice coachpainter. Various jobs over the next few years came to nothing but he had begun to write.

His first published poem appeared in the *Bulletin* in 1887 and many more pieces followed in Louisa's newspapers. Her best known venture, *Dawn*, published many mother-son collaborations under the pseudonym 'Archie Lawson' and eventually published his first major short story collection, *Short Stories in Prose and Verse* in 1894. Inspired by a trip through drought-stricken western New South Wales in 1892, this collection included what are now regarded as some of his finest works. The sights he saw out west, where 'men tramp and beg and live like dogs', spurred his creative imagination and he once again worked as a journalist on his return to Sydney.

By 1896 Lawson was on the threshold of professional and personal success. In that year two of his books published by Angus & Robertson, *In the Days When the World was Wide and Other Verses*, and *While the Billy Boils*, received critical acclaim and he married Bertha Bredt after a whirlwind romance. The years between these events and his departure from London, and further critical success, in 1900 established Lawson's reputation as a colourful figure in Sydney's Bohemian circles, especially when in the company of the notorious Dawn and Dusk Club.

In later years, Lawson described his years in London as a time of personal catastrophe that 'wracked and ruined' him, but it was during this period that he wrote *Joe Wilson and His Mates* (1901)—four thematically linked stories regarded by critics as the peak of his literary achievement.

Lawson's Commonwealth-State funeral is testimony to the recognition of an Australian writer already legendary at the time of his death.

'The Drover's Wife', considered to have been inspired by the years with his mother on their selection, 'A Day on a Selection', 'The Loaded Dog' and the Mitchell stories are considered, in the sparseness of their style, to represent the foundation of an Australian literature.

DOROTHY GAUVIN

HENRY LAWSON'S BUSH BALLADS

INTRODUCTION

This selection of Lawson's work is necessarily limited, so you may find that some of your favourites are missing. I hope you will feel that that is compensated by this first-ever gathering together of some of my earliest oil paintings.

The choice of poems and stories for this volume was to some degree dictated by the need to connect them with the paintings, which were chosen on the basis of the series or periods most often asked about. They cover my work from 1969, when I made my first tentative experiments with oils, through to 1984 when I began the *Banjo Paterson's People* series.

Although I had been drawing and painting in mixed media since before I started primary school, the lack of both money for materials and availability of tutoring meant that I came to oils rather late in my painting life. By the time I could afford to start with oils, I happened to be living even further out in the country so my first efforts were by trial and error—mostly error.

Yet there is a painting from that period of 1969, six years before I began to show my work in public, which is included here. 'The Drought Tree' was the second oil painting I attempted and was a gift to my husband's parents, who still value it above any in their collection. This very early painting accompanies Lawson's 'The Romance of the Swag'.

In 1970, my husband and I relocated to Brisbane, where I was finally able to find professional tutorship. I began attending life classes, sweating to produce an accurate representation of the human figure in the time allotted by the stop watch. I began to build an extensive library on anatomical drawing and the craft aspects of painting in oils.

About this time the relentless progress of rheumatoid arthritis ended my ability to work alongside my husband in his newsagency, a most demanding business requiring very long hours. However, my newly sedentary life meant more time available for painting. After my studies were completed, I spent the next few years alone in my basement studio, adapting what I had learned of technique to the ideas I longed to express. This long and careful 'apprenticeship in solitude' was favourably noted by the critic Frederick Rogers in his review, published in the *Sunday Mail*, Brisbane, in April 1978, of my first solo exhibition in Brisbane.

Before that exhibition, however, my first major series, titled 'Bush Memories', was exhibited in group shows on the Gold Coast, Toowoomba and Brisbane. I was overjoyed and also very nervous at being invited to show alongside such fine and well-known painters as Hugh Sawrey and Patrick Kilvington, who was kind enough to twice send me messages of congratulations, a generous encouragement to a newcomer.

Painted during 1976 and 1977, this series presented my bush characters' dreams of the past as a montage of images, an effect that I was to take up again ten years later for the *Banjo Paterson's Australians* series and one which I am still developing and refining.

Throughout my childhood, I had entered many competitions for drawing and painting and some years ago, my mother presented me with a boxful of first-prize certificates she had saved for me. One I still feel proud of was for a portrait prize, competing with professional artists, at age twelve. But it was not until 1977 that I tried my luck again and won first prize in the traditional sector at Garden City in Brisbane.

Even now, I have to laugh, recalling the surprise on the judge's face when I stepped up to claim the prize. Into the microphone he expressed his belief that the artist must have been a man, because of 'the courageous use of colour and the gutsiness of the brushwork'. I tackled him about old-fashioned attitudes, with my husband, Carl, beside me, grinning from ear to ear. A few years later, I met up with the judge again; we became painting friends and I ended up doing his portrait.

Later that same year, there came a phone call from my framer to say that the director of one of Brisbane's most successful galleries wished me to call him, having seen some of my work awaiting framing in the workshop. That phone call resulted in the mounting of my first solo show, 'The Australians', in 1978. Some of those who purchased pictures from that exhibition are still collectors of my work.

During this period, I fulfilled several private commissions for portraits and one officially commissioned portrait which hangs in Parliament House, Brisbane. These were interesting projects but my true love remained the telling of a human story and I embarked on the research for the series I called 'Convict Women of Eagle Farm'.

In my usual 'bull at a gate' style, I increased my working day from 12 to 15 hours, seven days a week, and the inevitable result was a flare-up of the arthritis, resulting in three months in bed. When I could be moved, Carl relocated us to Cairns, where he had grown up and where he knew I would benefit from the year-round warmth and quiet pace of life.

After a year or so of physiotherapy I was walking normally again, although with canes. About this time, I was also driving again, though to my disgust, I was demoted to an automatic gear shift.

Since my style of painting demands constant standing and pacing back and forth from the easel, it was some time before I resumed work. In late 1980, my exhibition titled 'Faces and Places' went on show at Raintrees in Cairns. One of these paintings, 'The Carpenter', accompanies that evocative piece Lawson called 'Drought-Stricken'. I hope you will agree that this painting might well evoke Henry Lawson's father, Niels Hertzberg Larsen, known in Australia as Peter Larsen, who is so tenderly described by his son in this recollection.

Following the success of the Cairns showing, I mounted a second solo exhibition in Brisbane. For this new series, I had conceived the idea of showing my characters in 'clownface', underscoring my view of such familiar institutions as 'The General', 'The Pop Star' and many others. This exhibition was also reviewed by Frederick Rogers, whose article for the *Courier Mail*, Brisbane, in June 1981 began: 'It is three years since Dorothy Gauvin's first exhibition made an impact rarely achieved by a hitherto unknown artist.' One of these paintings, 'The Critic', is shown with Lawson's tongue-in-cheek reply of the creative artist to those who make a living by writing about his achievement.

In 1982 my entry for the Castlemaine–Perkins competition was awarded first prize for the sector 'People in Pubs'. That year also saw the completion of my 'Convict Women' series.

This exhibition, again in Brisbane, gave me the shock of my life; all of the pictures were sold within two hours on the opening night, something we painters usually only dream about happening. Two of these paintings accompany Lawson's searing poem, 'One Hundred and Three', a finely drawn portrait of prison life as he himself had experienced it. Because of my own habit of optimism, my approach to this subject focused on portraying the support, the 'mateship' if you like, that a community of women is capable of extending to each other when faced with common troubles.

The camp journals and diaries that I researched for this series at the Mitchell Library, Sydney, and the Oxley Library in Brisbane, gave only the bare statistics but we can all imagine the personal stories that must lie beneath the dry records. A unique footnote to our history is the use of female convicts to cut rock and build roads, parts of which can still be seen in Brisbane today. The women planted maize and other crops at Eagle Farm and tended flocks of sheep. Little known is the fact that gangs of them were yoked to ploughs, tilling fields in a colony where horses and oxen were in shorter supply than human slave labour. Two paintings depicting these scenes are shown with the poem, 'The Men Who Made Australia', for it is interesting to remember the contribution of women to this work.

That year ended, however, on a low note. The day before Christmas, it was discovered that I had lost all central vision in one eye. Most of 1983 was taken up with medical investigations to discover the cause and possible treatment. Despite the best advice in Cairns, Brisbane and Sydney, and from the eye clinic in Los Angeles, the bottom line was: nothing could be done. Then, a short time later, our son sustained horrific head injuries in a freak accident while rock climbing. Despite brain surgery and an extensive stay in hospital, Paul was back at work within six months; a tribute to the quality of medical care he received and also to his own wonderful constitution and positive attitude.

Naturally, there were few paintings completed that year and strangely enough, some of these were landscapes, very rare in my body of work. Four of these are reproduced in this book. Also included is a rare romantic piece which was privately commissioned.

No anthology of Henry Lawson's work would be complete without his famous 'Faces in the Street' and for this I have selected the painting called 'The Dramatist'. It does not, of course, portray Lawson himself, but is a generic representation of that group of writers of whom Lawson, though not a playwright, is surely a member.

The paintings 'Aboriginal Stockman' and 'Rodeo' come from a small collection inspired by the fine horsemanship for which these men on the outback stations were renowned, and by my fascination with how they adapted their traditional hunting skills to the husbandry of domestic stock. 'The Bush Mate' is one of many paintings that resulted from listening to my father's tales of his life as a young man, working on a cattle station in central Queensland. Dad told me that after some days alone, riding the boundaries, he would sometimes get so lonely for the sound of a human voice that he would set his hat on a fence post and yarn away to it.

By 1987, the response to the *Banjo Paterson's People* series enabled me to establish my private studio-gallery which now exclusively handles the purchase of my paintings. Currently, I am working on a series based on Australian people and events of the 1890s, a very exciting period of our history.

While compiling this book, I came across Lawson's marvellous essay entitled 'If I Could Paint' which could stand as the blueprint for my own heart's goal: 'My ambition would be to paint Australia as it is, and as it changes; pictures that Australians could look through . . . onward to a brighter and nobler future.'

Dorothy Gauvin
Cairns, 1991

THE CITY BUSHMAN
(IN ANSWER TO 'BANJO' AND OTHERWISE)

It was pleasant up the country, City Bushman, where you went,
For you sought the greener patches and you travelled like a gent;
And you curse the trams and buses and the turmoil and the push,
Though you know the squalid city needn't keep you from the bush;
But we lately heard you singing of the 'plains where shade is not',
And you mentioned it was dusty—'all was dry and all was hot'.

True, the bush 'hath moods and changes'—and the bushman hath 'em, too,
For he's not a poet's dummy—he's a man, the same as you;
But his back is growing rounder—slaving for the absentee—
And his toiling wife is thinner than a country wife should be.
For we noticed that the faces of the folks we chanced to meet
Should have made a greater contrast to the faces in the street;
And, in short, we think the bushman's being driven to the wall,
And it's doubtful if his spirit will be 'loyal thro' it all'.

Though the bush has been romantic and it's nice to sing about,
There's a lot of patriotism that the land could do without—
Sort of BRITISH WORKMAN nonsense that shall perish in the scorn
Of the drover who is driven and the shearer who is shorn,
Of the struggling western farmers who have little time for rest,
And are ruined on selections in the sheep-infested West;
Droving songs are very pretty, but they merit little thanks
From the people of a country in possession of the Banks.

And the 'rise and fall of seasons' suits the rise and fall of rhyme,
But we know that western seasons do not run on schedule time;
For the drought will go on drying while there's anything to dry,
Then it rains until you'd fancy it would bleach the sunny sky—
Then it pelters out of reason, for the downpour day and night
Nearly sweeps the population to the Great Australian Bight.
It is up in Northern Queensland that the seasons do their best,
But it's doubtful if you ever saw a season in the West;
There are years without an autumn or a winter or a spring,
There are broiling Junes, and summers when it rains like anything.

STATION BOSS

SERIES: BUSH MEMORIES, 1976/77
DIMENSIONS: 60.9 X 45.7 CM

In the bush my ears were opened to the singing of the bird,
But the 'carol of the magpie' was a thing I never heard.
Once the beggar roused my slumbers in a shanty, it is true,
But I only heard him asking, 'Who the blanky blank are you?'
And the bell-bird in the ranges—but his 'silver chime' is harsh
When it's heard beside the solo of the curlew in the marsh.

Yes, I heard the shearers singing 'William Riley', out of tune,
Saw 'em fighting round a shanty on a Sunday afternoon,
But the bushman isn't always 'trapping brumbies in the night',
Nor is he for ever riding when 'the morn is fresh and bright',
And he isn't always singing in the humpies on the run—
And the camp-fire's 'cheery blazes' are a trifle overdone;
We have grumbled with the bushmen round the fire on rainy days,
When the smoke would blind a bullock and there wasn't any blaze,
Save the blazes of our language, for we cursed the fire in turn
Till the atmosphere was heated and the wood began to burn.
Then we had to wring our blueys which were rotting in the swags,
And we saw the sugar leaking through the bottoms of the bags,
And we couldn't raise a chorus, for the toothache and the cramp,
While we spent the hours of darkness draining puddles round the camp.

Would you like to change with Clancy—go-a-droving? tell us true,
For we rather think that Clancy would be glad to change with you,
And be something in the city; but 'twould give your muse a shock
To be losing time and money through the foot-rot in the flock,
And you wouldn't mind the beauties underneath the starry dome
If you had a wife and children and a lot of bills at home.

Did you ever guard the cattle when the night was inky-black,
And it rained, and icy water trickled gently down your back
Till your saddle-weary backbone fell a-aching to the roots
And you almost felt the croaking of the bull-frog in your boots—
Sit and shiver in the saddle, curse the restless stock and cough
Till a squatter's irate dummy cantered up to warn you off?
Did you fight the drought and pleuro when the 'seasons' were asleep,
Felling she-oaks all the morning for a flock of starving sheep,
Drinking mud instead of water—climbing trees and lopping boughs
For the broken-hearted bullocks and the dry and dusty cows?

IT'LL RAIN

SERIES: THE AUSTRALIANS, 1978
DIMENSIONS: 71.1 x 55.9 CM

15

Do you think the bush was better in the 'good old droving days',
When the squatter ruled supremely as the king of western ways,
When you got a slip of paper for the little you could earn,
But were forced to take provisions from the station in return—
When you couldn't keep a chicken at your humpy on the run,
For the squatter wouldn't let you—and your work was never done;
When you had to leave the missus in a lonely hut forlorn
While you 'rose up Willy Riley'—in the days ere you were born?

Ah! we read about the drovers and the shearers and the like
Till we wonder why such happy and romantic fellows strike.
Don't you fancy that the poets ought to give the bush a rest
Ere they raise a just rebellion in the over-written West?
Where the simple-minded bushman gets a meal and bed and rum
Just by riding round reporting phantom flocks that never come;
Where the scalper—never troubled by the 'war-whoop of the push'—
Has a quiet little billet—breeding rabbits in the bush;
Where the idle shanty-keeper never fails to make a draw,
And the dummy gets his tucker through provisions in the law;
Where the labour-agitator—when the shearers rise in might—
Makes his money sacrificing all his substance for The Right;
Where the squatter makes his fortune, and 'the seasons rise and fall',
And the poor and honest bushman has to suffer for it all;
Where the drovers and the shearers and the bushmen and the rest
Never reach the Eldorado of the poets of the West.

And you think the bush is purer and that life is better there,
But it doesn't seem to pay you like the 'squalid street and square'.
Pray inform us, City Bushman, where you read, in prose or verse,
Of the awful 'city urchin who would greet you with a curse'.
There are golden hearts in gutters, though their owners lack the fat,
And we'll back a teamster's offspring to outswear a city brat.
Do you think we're never jolly where the trams and buses rage?
Did you hear the gods in chorus when 'Ri-tooral' held the stage?
Did you catch a ring of sorrow in the city urchin's voice
When he yelled for Billy Elton, when he thumped the floor for Royce?
Do the bushmen, down on pleasure, miss the everlasting stars
When they drink and flirt and so on in the glow of private bars?

JONDARYAN WOOLSHED

Series: Places and Faces, 1980
Dimensions: 30.4 x 50.8 cm

You've a down on 'trams and buses', or the 'roar' of 'em, you said,
And the 'filthy, dirty attic', where you never toiled for bread.
(And about that self-same attic—Lord! wherever have you been?
For the struggling needlewoman mostly keeps her attic clean.)
But you'll find it very jolly with the cuff-and-collar push,
And the city seems to suit you, while you rave about the bush.

You'll admit that Up-the-Country, more especially in drought,
Isn't quite the Eldorado that the poets rave about,
Yet at times we long to gallop where the reckless bushman rides
In the wake of startled brumbies that are flying for their hides;
Long to feel the saddle tremble once again between our knees
And to hear the stockwhips rattle just like rifles in the trees!
Long to feel the bridle-leather tugging strongly in the hand
And to feel once more a little like a native of the land.
And the ring of bitter feeling in the jingling of our rhymes
Isn't suited to the country nor the spirit of the times.
Let us go together droving, and returning, if we live,
Try to understand each other while we reckon up the div.

A MINDEN FARM

SERIES: LANDSCAPES, 1982/83
DIMENSIONS: 55.8 x 91.4 CM

THE ROARING DAYS

The night too quickly passes
  And we are growing old,
So let us fill our glasses
  And toast the Days of Gold;
When finds of wondrous treasure
  Set all the South ablaze,
And you and I were faithful mates
  All through the roaring days!

Then stately ships came sailing
  From every harbour's mouth,
And sought the land of promise
  That beaconed in the South;
Then southward streamed their streamers
  And swelled their canvas full
To speed the wildest dreamers
  E'er borne in vessel's hull.

Their shining Eldorado,
  Beneath the southern skies,
Was day and night for ever
  Before their eager eyes.
The brooding bush, awakened,
  Was stirred in wild unrest,
And all the year a human stream
  Went pouring to the West.

The rough bush roads re-echoed
  The bar-room's noisy din,
When troops of stalwart horsemen
  Dismounted at the inn.
And oft the hearty greetings
  And hearty clasp of hands
Would tell of sudden meetings
  Of friends from other lands;

When, puzzled long, the new-chum
  Would recognise at last,
Behind a bronzed and bearded skin,
  A comrade of the past.

And when the cheery camp-fire
  Explored the bush with gleams,
The camping-grounds were crowded
  With caravans of teams;
Then home the jests were driven,
  And good old songs were sung,
And choruses were given
  The strength of heart and lung.
Oh, they were lion-hearted
  Who gave our country birth!
Oh, they were of the stoutest sons
  From all the lands on earth!

Oft when the camps were dreaming,
  And fires began to pale,
Through rugged ranges gleaming
  Would come the Royal Mail.
Behind six foaming horses,
  And lit by flashing lamps,
Old 'Cobb & Co's', in royal state,
  Went dashing past the camps.

Oh, who would paint the goldfield,
  And limn the picture right,
As we have often seen it
  In early morning's light;
The yellow mounds of mullock
  With spots of red and white,
The scattered quartz that glistened
  Like diamonds in light;

ABORIGINAL STOCKMAN

SERIES: BUSH MEMORIES, 1976/77
DIMENSIONS: 45.7 x 60.9 CM

The azure line of ridges,
    The bush of darkest green,
The little homes of calico
    That dotted all the scene.

I hear the fall of timber
    From distant flats and fells,
The pealing of the anvils
    As clear as little bells,
The rattle of the cradle,
    The clack of windlass-boles,
The flutter of the crimson flags
    Above the golden holes.

Ah, then their hearts were bolder,
    And if Dame Fortune frowned
Our swags we'd lightly shoulder
    And tramp to other ground.
But golden days are vanished,
    And altered is the scene;
The diggings are deserted,
    The camping-grounds are green;
The flaunting flag of progress
    In the West unfurled,
The mighty bush with iron rails
    Is tethered to the world.

RODEO

Series: Places and Faces, 1980
Dimensions: 71.1 x 50.8 cm

SAINT PETER

Now, I think there is a likeness
  'Twixt St Peter's life and mine,
For he did a lot of trampin'
  Long ago in Palestine.
He was 'union' when the workers
  First began to organise,
And—I'm glad that old St Peter
  Keeps the gate of Paradise.

When the ancient agitator
  And his brothers carried swags,
I've no doubt he very often
  Tramped with empty tucker-bags;
And I'm glad he's Heaven's picket,
  For I hate explainin' things,
And he'll think a union ticket
  Just as good as Whitely King's.

He denied the Saviour's union,
  Which was weak of him, no doubt;
But perhaps his feet was blistered
  And his boots had given out.
And the bitter storm was rushin'
  On the bark and on the slabs,
And a cheerful fire was blazin',
  And the hut was full of 'scabs'.

When I reach the great head-station—
  Which is somewhere 'off the track'—
I won't want to talk with angels
  Who have never been out back;
They might bother me with offers
  Of a banjo—meanin' well—
And a pair of wings to fly with,
  When I only want a spell.

I'll just ask for old St Peter,
  And I think, when he appears,
I will only have to tell him
  That I carried swag for years.
'I've been on the track,' I'll tell him,
  'An' I done the best I could,'
And he'll understand me better
  Than the other angels would.

He won't try to get a chorus
  Out of lungs that's worn to rags,
Or to graft the wings on shoulders
  That is stiff with humpin' swags.
But I'll rest about the station
  Where the work-bell never rings,
Till they blow the final trumpet
  And the Great Judge sees to things.

THE BUSH MATE

SERIES: BUSH MEMORIES, 1976/77
DIMENSIONS: 45.7 x 60.9 CM

A VOICE FROM THE CITY

On western plain and eastern hill
    Where once my fancy ranged,
The station hands are riding still
    And they are little changed.
But I have lost in London gloom
    The glory of the day,
The grand perfume of wattle bloom
    Is faint and far away.

Brown faces under broad-brimmed hats
    The grip of wiry hands,
The gallops on the frosty flats,
    Seem dreams of other lands;
The camp-fire and the stars that blaze
    Above the mystic plain
Are but the thoughts of vanished days
    That never come again.

The evening star I seldom view—
    That led me on to roam—
I never see the morning star
    That used to draw me home.
But I have often longed for day
    To hide the few I see,
Because they only point and say
    Most bitter things to me.

I wear my life on pavement stones
    That drag me ever down,
A paltry slave to little things,
    By custom chained to town.
I've lost the strength to strike alone,
    The heart to do and dare—
I mind the day I'd roll my swag
    And tramp to—God-knows-where.

When I should wait I wander out,
    When I should go I bide—
I scarcely dare to think about
    The days when I could ride.
I would not mount before his eyes,
    'Straight' Bushman tall and tan—
I mind the day when I stood up
    And fought him like a man.

I mind the time when I was shy
    To meet the brown Bush girls—
I've lunched with lords since then and I
    Have been at home with earls:
I learned to smile and learned to bow
    And lie to ladies gay—
But to a gaunt Bushwoman now
    I'd not know what to say.

And if I sought her hard bare home,
    From scenes of show and sham,
I'd sit all ill at ease and feel
    The poor weak thing I am.
I could not meet her hopeless eyes
    That look one through and through,
The haggard woman of the past
    Who once thought I was true.

But nought on earth can last for aye,
    And wild with care and pain,
Some day by chance I'll break away
    And seek the Bush again.
And find awhile from bitter years
    The rest the Bush can bring,
And hear, perhaps, with truer ears
    The songs it has to sing.

THE OLD PLACE

Series: The Australians, 1978
Dimensions: 50.8 x 60.9 cm

When the 'Army' Prays for Watty

When the kindly hours of darkness, save for light of moon and star,
Hide the picture on the signboard over Doughty's Horse Bazaar;
When the last rose-tint is fading on the distant mulga scrub,
Then the Army prays for Watty at the entrance of his pub.

Now, I often sit at Watty's when the night is very near,
With a head that's full of jingles and the fumes of bottled beer,
For I always have a fancy that, if I am over there
When the Army prays for Watty, I'm included in the prayer.

Watty lounges in his arm-chair, in its old accustomed place,
With a fatherly expression on his round and passive face;
And his arms are clasped before him in a calm, contented way,
And he nods his head and dozes when he hears the Army pray.

And I wonder does he ponder on the distant years and dim,
Or his chances over yonder, when the Army prays for him?
Has he not a fear connected with the warm place down below,
Where, according to good Christians, all the publicans should go?

But his features give no token of a feeling in his breast,
Save of peace that is unbroken and a conscience well at rest;
And we guzzle as we guzzled long before the Army came,
And the loafers wait for 'shouters' and—they get there just the same.

It would take a lot of praying—lots of thumping on the drum—
To prepare our sinful, straying, erring souls for Kingdom Come;
But I love my fellow-sinners, and I hope, upon the whole,
That the Army gets a hearing when it prays for Watty's soul.

WAITIN' TILL SHE OPENS

Series: The Australians, 1978
Dimensions: 60.9 x 45.7 cm

A Day on a Selection

The scene is a small New South Wales western selection, the holder whereof is native-English. His wife is native-Irish. Time, Sunday, about 8 a.m. A used-up looking woman comes from the slab-and-bark house, turns her face towards the hillside, and shrieks: 'T-o-o-m-*may!*'

No response, and presently she draws a long breath and screams again: '*Tom*-m-a-a-y!'

A faint echo comes from far up the siding where Tommy's presence is vaguely indicated by half-a-dozen cows moving slowly—very slowly—down towards the cow-yard.

The woman retires. Ten minutes later she comes out again and screams: '*Tom*my!'

'Y-e-e-a-s-s!' very passionately and shrilly.

'Ain't you goin' to bring those cows down to-day?'

'Y-e-e-a-s-s-s!—carn't yer see I'm comin'?'

A boy is seen to run wildly along the siding and hurl a missile at a feeding cow; the cow runs forward a short distance through the trees, and then stops to graze again while the boy stirs up another milker.

An hour goes by.

The rising Australian generation is represented by a thin, lanky youth of about fifteen. He is milking. The cow-yard is next to the house, and is mostly ankle-deep in slush. The boy drives a dusty, discouraged-looking cow into the bail, and pins her head there, then he gets tackle on to her right hind leg, hauls it back, and makes it fast to the fence. There are eleven cows, but not one of them can be milked out of the bail—chiefly because their teats are sore. The selector does not know what makes the teats sore, but he has an unquestioning faith in a certain ointment, recommended to him by a man who knows less about cows than he does himself, which he causes to be applied at irregular intervals—leaving the mode of application to the discretion of his son. Meanwhile the teats remain sore.

Having made the cow fast, the youngster cautiously takes hold of the least sore teat, yanks it suddenly, and dodges the cow's hock. When he gets enough milk to dip his dirty hands in, he moistens the teats, and things go on more smoothly. Now and then he relieves the monotony of his occupation by squirting at the eye of a calf which is dozing in the adjacent pen. Other times he milks into his mouth. Every time the cow kicks, a burr or a grass-seed or a bit of something else falls into the milk, and the boy drowns these things with a well-directed stream—on the principle that what's out of sight is out of mind.

THE HOUSE COW

Series: Places and Faces, 1980
Dimensions: 50.8 x 66 cm

Sometimes the boy sticks his head into the cow's side, hangs on by a teat, and dozes, while the bucket, mechanically gripped between his knees, sinks lower and lower till it rests on the ground. Likely as not he'll doze on until his mother's shrill voice startles him with an enquiry as to whether he intends to get that milking done to-day; other times he is roused by the plunging of the cow, or knocked over by a calf which has broken through a defective panel in the pen. In the latter case the youth gets tackle on to the calf, detaches its head from the teat with the heel of his boot, and makes it fast somewhere. Sometimes the cow breaks or loosens the leg-rope and gets her leg into the bucket and then the youth clings desperately to the pail and hopes she'll get her hoof out again without spilling the milk. Sometimes she does, more often she doesn't—it depends on the strength of the boy and the pail and on the strategy of the former. Anyway, the boy will lam the cow down with a jagged yard shovel, let her out, and bail up another.

When he considers that he has finished milking he lets the cows out with their calves and carries the milk down to the dairy, where he has a heated argument with his mother, who—judging from the quantity of milk—has reason to believe that he has slummed some of the milkers. This he indignantly denies, telling her she knows very well the cows are going dry.

The dairy is built of rotten box bark—though there is plenty of good stringy-bark within easy distance—and the structure looks as if it wants to lie down and is only prevented by three crooked props on the leaning side; more props will soon be needed in the rear for the dairy shows signs of going in that direction. The milk is set in dishes made of kerosene tins, cut in halves, which are placed on bark shelves fitted round against the walls. The shelves are not level and the dishes are brought to a comparatively horizontal position by means of chips and bits of bark, inserted under the lower side. The milk is covered by soiled sheets of old newspapers supported on sticks laid across the dishes. This protection is necessary because the box bark in the roof has crumbled away and left fringed holes—also because the fowls roost up there. Sometimes the paper sags, and the cream may have to be scraped off an article on dairy farming.

The selector's wife removes the newspapers, and reveals a thick, yellow layer of rich cream, plentifully peppered with dust that has drifted in somehow. She runs a forefinger round the edges of the cream to detach it from the tin, wipes her finger in her mouth, and skims. If the milk and cream are very thick she rolls the cream over like a pancake with her fingers, and lifts it out in sections. The thick milk is poured into a slop-bucket, for the pigs and calves, the dishes are 'cleaned'—by the aid of a dipper full of warm water and a rag—and the wife proceeds to set the morning's milk. Tom holds up the doubtful-looking rag that serves as a strainer while his mother pours in the milk. Sometimes the boy's hands get tired and he lets some of the milk run over, and gets into trouble; but it doesn't matter much, for the straining-cloth has several sizeable holes in the middle.

The door of the dairy faces the dusty road and is off its hinges and has to be propped up. The prop is missing this morning, and Tommy is accused of having been seen chasing old Poley with it at an earlier hour. He never see'd the damn prop, never chased no cow with it, and wants to know what's the use of always accusing him. He further complains that he's always blamed for everything. The pole is not forthcoming, and so an old dray is backed against the door to keep it in position. There is more trouble about a cow that is lost, and hasn't been milked for two days. The boy takes the cows up to the paddock slip-rails and lets the top rail down; the lower rail fits rather tightly and some exertion is required to free it, so he makes the animals jump that one. Then he 'poddies'—hand-feeds— the calves which have been weaned too early. He carries the skim-milk to the yard in a bucket made out of an oil drum—sometimes a kerosene tin—seizes a calf by the nape of the neck with his left hand, inserts the dirty forefinger of his right into its mouth, and shoves its head down into the milk. The calf sucks, thinking it has a teat, and pretty soon it butts violently—as calves do to remind their mothers to let down the milk—and the boy's wrist gets barked against the jagged edge of the bucket. He welts that calf in the jaw, kicks it in the stomach, tries to smother it with its nose in the milk, and finally dismisses it with the assistance of the calf rope and a shovel, and gets another. His hand feels sticky and the cleaned finger makes it look as if he wore a filthy, greasy glove with the forefinger torn off.

The selector himself is standing against a fence talking to a neighbour. His arms rest on the top rail of the fence, his chin rests on his hands, his pipe rests between his fingers, and his eyes rest on a white cow that is chewing her cud on the opposite side of the fence. The neighbour's arms rest on the top rail also, his chin rests on his hands, his pipe rests between his fingers, and his eyes rest on the cow. They are talking about that cow. They have been talking about her for three hours. She is chewing her cud. Her nose is well up and forward, and her eyes are shut. She lets her lower jaw fall a little, moves it to one side, lifts it again, and brings it back into position with a springing kind of jerk that has almost a visible recoil. Then her jaws stay perfectly still for a moment, and you would think she had stopped chewing. But she hasn't. Now and again a soft, easy, smooth-going swallow passes visibly along her clean, white throat and disappears. She chews again, and by-and-by she loses consciousness and forgets to chew. She never opens her eyes. She is young and in good condition; she has had enough to eat, the sun is just properly warm for her, and—well, if an animal can be really happy, she ought to be.

Presently the two men drag themselves away from the fence, fill their pipes, and go to have a look at some rows of forked sticks, apparently stuck in the ground for some purpose. The selector calls these sticks fruit-trees, and he calls the place 'the orchard'. They fool round these wretched sticks until dinner-time, when the neighbour says he must be getting home. 'Stay and have some dinner! Man alive! Stay and have some dinner!' says the selector; and so the friend stays.

It is a broiling hot day in summer, and the dinner consists of hot roast meat, hot baked potatoes, hot cabbage, hot pumpkin, hot peas, and burning-hot plum-pudding. The family drinks on an average four cups of tea each per meal. The wife takes her place at the head of the table with a broom to keep the fowls out, and at short intervals she interrupts the conversation with such exclamations as 'Shoo! shoo!', 'Tommy, can't you see that fowl? Drive it out!' The fowls evidently pass a lot of their time in the house. They mark the circle described by the broom, and take care to keep two or three inches beyond it. Every now and then you see a fowl on the dresser amongst the crockery, and there is great concern to get it out before it breaks something. While dinner is in progress two steers get into the wheat through a broken rail which has been spliced with stringy-bark, and a calf or two break into the vineyard. And yet this careless Australian selector, who is too shiftless to put up a decent fence, or build a decent house, and who knows little or nothing about farming, would seem by his conversation to have read up all the great social and political questions of the day. Here are some fragments of conversation caught at the dinner-table. Present—the selector, the missus, the neighbour, Corney George—nicknamed 'Henry George'—Tommy, Jacky, and the younger children. The spaces represent interruptions by the fowls and children:

Corney George (continuing conversation): 'But Henry George says, in "Progress and Poverty", he says—'

Missus (to the fowls); 'Shoo! Shoo!'

Corney: 'He says—'

Tom: 'Marther, jist speak to this Jack.'

Missus (to Jack): 'If you can't behave yourself, leave the table.'

Tom: 'He says in "Progress and—" '

Missus: 'Shoo!'

Neighbour: 'I think "Lookin' Backwards" is more—'

Missus: 'Shoo! Shoo! Tom, can't you see that fowl?'

Selector: 'Now I think "Caesar's Column" is more likely—Just look at—'

Missus: 'Shoo! Shoo!'

Selector: 'Just look at the French Revolution.'

Corney: 'Now, Henry George—'

Tom: 'Marther! I seen a old-man kangaroo up on—'

Missus: 'Shut up! Eat your dinner an' hold your tongue. Carn't you see someone's speakin'?'

Selector: 'Just look at the French—'

Missus (to the fowls): 'Shoo! Shoo!' (turning suddenly and unexpectedly on Jacky): 'Take your fingers out of the sugar!—Blast yer! that I should say such a thing.'

Neighbour: 'But "Lookin' Back'ards"—'

Missus: 'There you go, Tom! Didn't I say you'd spill that tea? Go away from the table!'

Selector: 'I think "Caesar's Column" is the only natural—'

Missus: 'Shoo! Shoo!' She loses patience, gets up and fetches a young rooster with the flat of the broom, sending him flying into the yard; he falls with his head towards the door and starts in again. Later on the conversation is about Deeming.

Selector: 'There's no doubt the man's mad—'

Missus: 'Deeming! That Windsor wretch! Why, if I was in the law I'd have him boiled alive! Don't tell me he didn't know what he was doing! Why, I'd have him—'

Corney: 'But, missus, you—'

Missus (to the fowls): 'Shoo! Shoo!'

THE SHEARER'S DREAM

Mitchell and I rolled up our swags after New Year and started to tramp west. It had been a very bad season after a long drought. Old Baldy Thompson had only shorn a few bales of grass seed and burrs, so he said, and thought of taking the track himself; but we hoped to get on shearing stragglers at West-o'-Sunday or one of the stations of the Hungerford track.

It was very hot weather, so we started after sunset, intending to travel all night. We crossed the big billabong, and were ploughing through the dust and sand towards West Bourke, when a buggy full of city girls and swells passed by. They were part of a theatrical company on tour in the Back-Blocks, and some local Johnnies. They'd been driven out to see an artesian bore, or wool-shed, or something. The horses swerved, and jerked a little squawk out of one of the girls. Then another said:

'Ow-w! Two old swaggies. He! he! he!'

I glanced at Mitchell to see if he was hit, and caught his head down; but he pulled himself up and pretended to hitch his swag into an easier position.

About a hundred yards further on he gave me a side look and said:

'Did that touch you, Harry?'

'No,' I said, and I laughed.

'You see,' reflected Mitchell, 'they're more to be pitied than blamed. It's their ignorance. In the first place, we're not two old tramps, as they think. We are professional shearers; and the Australian shearers are about the most independent and intelligent class of men in the world. We've got more genius in one of our little fingers than there is in the whole of that waggonette-load of diddle-daddle and fiddle-faddle and giggles. Their intellects are on a level with the rotten dramas they travel with, and their lives about as false. They are slaves to the public, and their home is the pub parlour, with sickly, senseless Johnnies to shout suppers and drink for them and lend their men money. If one of those girls is above the average, how she must despise those Johnnies—and the life! She must feel a greater contempt for them than the private barmaid does for the boozer she cleans out. He gets his drink and some enjoyment, anyhow. And how she must loathe the life she leads! And what's the end of it as often as not? I remember once, when I was a boy, I was walking out with two aunts of mine—they're both dead now. God rest their fussy, innocent old souls!—and one of 'em said suddenly, "Look! Quick, Jack! There's Maggie So-and-So, the great actress." And I looked and saw a woman training vines in a porch. It seemed like seeing an angel to me, and

SULKY REMAINS

SERIES: LANDSCAPES, 1982/83
DIMENSIONS: 40.6 x 55.8 CM

I never forgot her as she was then. The diggers used to go miles out of town to meet the coach that brought her, and take the horses out and drag it in, and throw gold in her lap, and worship her.

'The last time I was in Sydney I saw her sitting in the back parlour of a third rate pub. She was dying of dropsy and couldn't move from her chair. She showed me a portrait of herself as I remembered her, and talked quite seriously about going on the stage again.

'Now, our home is about two thousand miles wide, and the world's our stage. If the worst comes to the worst we can always get tucker and wood and water for nothing. If we're camping at a job in a tent there's no house-cleaning to bother us. All we've got to do when the camp gets too dirty is to shift the tent to a fresh place. We've got time to think and—we're free.

'But then, agen,' he reflected, 'there's the world's point of view to be considered. Some day I might be flashing past in a buggy or saloon carriage—or, the chances are it will be you—and you might look out the window and see an old swaggy tramping along in the dust, or camped under a strip of calico in the rain in the scrub. (And it might be me—old Mitchell—that really wrote your books, only the world won't know it.) And then you'll realise what a wretched, miserable life it was. We never realise the miseries of life till we look back—the mistakes and miseries that had to be and couldn't be helped. It's all luck—luck and chance.'

But those girls seemed to have gravelled Mitchell, and he didn't seem able to talk himself round. He tramped on, brooding for a while, and then suddenly he said:

'Look here, Harry! Those girls are giving a dance to-night, and if I liked to go back to Bourke and tog up and go to the dance I could pick out the prettiest, dance with her all the evening, and take her for a stroll afterwards, old tramp as they thought me. I've lived—But it wouldn't be worth my while now.'

I'd seen Jack in a mood like this before, and thought it best to say nothing. Perhaps the terrible heat had affected him a little. We walked on in silence until we came to the next billabong. 'Best boil the billy here, Harry,' said Mitchell, 'and have some tea before we go any further.'

I got some sticks together and made a fire and put the billy on. The country looked wretched—like the ghost of a burnt-out land—in the moonlight. The banks of the creek were like ashes, the thin, gnarled gum-bush seemed dry-rotting fast, and in many places the surface of the ground was cracked in squares where it had shrunk in the drought. In the bed of the creek was a narrow gutter of water that looked like bad milk.

Mitchell sat on his swag, with his pint of tea on the ground by his foot, and chewed his pipe.

'What's up, Jack?' I asked. 'Have you got the blues?'

'Well, yes, Harry,' he said. 'I'm generally dull the first day on the track. The first day is generally the worst, anywhere or anytime—except, perhaps, when you're married . . . I got—Well, I got thinking of the time when a woman's word could have hurt me.'

Just then one of the 'travellers' who were camped a bit up the creek suddenly commenced to sing. It was a song called 'The Shearer's Dream', and I suppose the buggy of girls, or the conversation they started, reminded him of it. He started his verses and most of his lines with a howl; and there were unexpected howls all through the song, and it wailed off, just as unexpectedly, in places where there was no pathos that I could see:

'Oh, I dreamt I shore in a shearer's shed, and it was a dream of joy,
For every one of the rouseabouts was a girl dressed up as a boy—
Dressed up like a page in a pantomime, and the prettiest ever seen—
They had flaxen hair, they had coal-black hair—and every shade between.'

'Every' with sudden and great energy, a long drop on to 'shade', and a wail of intense sadness and regret running on into 'between', the dirge reaching its wailsomest in the 'tween' in every case.

'The shed was cooled by electric fans that was over every "shoot";
The pens was of polished ma-ho-gany, and ev'rything else to suit;
The huts was fixed with spring mattresses, and the tucker was simply grand,
And every night by the biller-bong we darnced to a German band.'

'*Chorus, boys!*'

'There was short, plump girls, there was tall, slim girls, and the handsomest
    ever seen—
They was four-foot-five, they was six-foot high, and hevery size between.

'Our pay was the wool on the jumbucks' backs, so we shore till all was blue—
The sheep was washed afore they was shore (and the rams was scented too);
And we all of us cried when the shed cut out, in spite of the long, hot days,
For hevery hour them girls waltzed in with whisky and beer on tr-a-a-a-ys!'

'*Chorus! you——!*'

'They had kind grey eyes, they had coal-black eyes, and the grandest
    ever seen—
They had plump pink hands, they had slim white hands, and hevery shape
    be-tw-e-e-en.

'There was three of them girls to every chap, and as jealous as they could be—'*

'Ow! you——'

The singer's voice or memory seemed suddenly to have failed him at this point, but whether his mates hit him on the back of the head with a tomahawk, or only choked him, I do not know. Mitchell was inclined to think, from the sound of it, that they choked him.

*'There was three of them girls to every chap, and six of 'em picked on me;
We was draftin' 'em out for the homeward track and sharin' 'em round like steam,
When I woke with my head in the blazin' sun to find 'twas a shearer's dream.'

POSTS AND RAILS

He stumbled up the ridges
    With his old cattle-dog;
He took his maul and wedges
    From underneath a log—
His wedges, maul and crosscut,
    So light to drive and draw;
And he rubbed well with suet
    The dew-rust on the saw.

He marked a tree and felled it,
    As lone-hand splitters do;
He measured it and cut it—
    The cuts were straight and true.
And all day in December,
    When dust and heat prevails,
From out the groaning timber
    He belted posts and rails.

He'd come across the water;
    His thoughts were far away—
His little fair-haired daughter
    Was buried yesterday,
And till the sun was setting,
    And milk-cows sought the yard,
He worked like one forgetting,
    And never worked so hard.

His hope was now a far light
    And dim across the seas;
He would have worked by starlight
    His aching heart to ease;
But up the dark'ning siding,
    Beneath the fading dome,
His eldest son came riding
    To take his father home.

The posts and rails are rotten,
    And vanished is the plough;
The homestead is forgotten—
    The place a 'stud farm' now.
And sullen touts are shirking,
    Where men, in days gone by,
Died hopeless, but died *working*,
    When their turn came to die.

I'd rather—oh, I'd a rather,
    When weary and way-worn,
My little foreign father
    Had died where he was born.
I know not what the curse is;
    But I, when daylight fails,
From long years of reverses
    Sit splitting posts and rails.

THE DAM

SERIES: LANDSCAPES, 1982/83
DIMENSIONS: 40.6 x 50.8 CM

SUNRISE ON THE RIVER

SERIES: LANDSCAPES, 1982/83
DIMENSIONS: 40.6 X 55.8 CM

SUNSET ON THE RIVER

SERIES: LANDSCAPES, 1982/83
DIMENSIONS: 45.7 x 76.2 CM

REEDY RIVER

Ten miles down Reedy River
    A pool of water lies,
And all the year it mirrors
    The changes in the skies,
And in that pool's broad bosom
    Is room for all the stars;
Its bed of sand has drifted
    O'er countless rocky bars.

Around the lower edges
    There waves a bed of reeds,
Where water rats are hidden
    And where the wild duck breeds;
And grassy slopes rise gently
    To ridges long and low,
Where groves of wattle flourish
    And native bluebells grow.

Beneath the granite ridges
    The eye may just discern
Where Rocky Creek emerges
    From deep green banks of fern;
And standing tall between them,
    The grassy she-oaks cool
The hard, blue-tinted waters
    Before they reach the pool.

Ten miles down Reedy River
    One Sunday afternoon,
I rode with Mary Campbell
    To that broad bright lagoon;
We left our horses grazing
    Till shadows climbed the peak,
And strolled beneath the she-oaks
    On the banks of Rocky Creek.

Then home along the river
    That night we rode a race,
And the moonlight lent a glory
    To Mary Campbell's face;
And I pleaded for my future
    All thro' that moonlight ride,
Until our weary horses
    Drew closer side by side.

Ten miles from Ryan's crossing
    And five miles below the peak,
I built a little homestead
    On the banks of Rocky Creek;
I cleared the land and fenced it
    And ploughed the rich red loam,
And my first crop was golden
    When I brought Mary home.

Now still down Reedy River
    The grassy she-oaks sigh,
And the waterholes still mirror
    The pictures in the sky;
And over all for ever
    Go sun and moon and stars,
While the golden sand is drifting
    Across the rocky bars;

But of the hut I builded
    There are no traces now.
And many rains have levelled
    The furrows of the plough;
And my bright days are olden,
    For the twisted branches wave
And the wattle blossoms golden
    On the hill by Mary's grave.

CLARENCE RIVER

SERIES: LANDSCAPES, 1982/83
DIMENSIONS: 45.7 x 71.1 CM

45

The Romance of the Swag

The Australian swag fashion is the easiest way in the world of carrying a load. I ought to know something about carrying loads: I've carried babies, which are the heaviest and most awkward and heart-breaking loads in this world for a boy or man to carry, I fancy. God remember mothers who slave about the housework (and do sometimes a man's work in addition in the Bush) with a heavy, squalling kid on one arm! I've humped logs on the Selection, 'burning off', with loads of fencing posts and rails and palings out of steep, rugged gullies (and was happier then, perhaps); I've carried a shovel, crowbar, heavy 'rammer', a dozen insulators on an average (strung round my shoulders with raw flax)—to say nothing of soldering kit, tucker bag, billy and climbing spurs—all day on a telegraph line in rough country in New Zealand, and in places where a man had to manage his load with one hand and help himself climb with the other; and I've helped hump and drag telegraph poles up cliffs and sidings where the horses couldn't go. I've carried a portmanteau on the hot dusty roads in green old Jackeroo days. Ask any actor who's been stranded and had to count railway sleepers from one town to another! he'll tell you what sort of an awkward load a portmanteau is, especially if there's a broken-hearted man underneath it. I've tried knapsack fashion—one of the least healthy and most likely to give a man sores; I've carried my belongings in a three-bushel sack slung over my shoulder—blankets, tucker, spare boots and poetry all lumped together. I tried carrying a load on my head, and got a crick in my neck and spine for days. I've carried a load on my mind that should have been shared by editors and publishers. I've helped hump luggage and furniture up to, and down from, a top flat in London. And I've carried swag for months outback in Australia—and it was life, in spite of its 'squalidness' and meanness and wretchedness and hardship, and in spite of the fact that the world would have regarded us as 'tramps'—and a free life amongst *men* from all the world!

The Australian swag was born of Australia and no other land—of the Great Lone Land of magnificent distances and bright heat; the land of Self-reliance, and Never-give-in, and Help-your-mate. The grave of many of the world's tragedies and comedies—royal and otherwise. The land where a man out of employment might shoulder his swag in Adelaide and take the track, and years later walk into a hut on the Gulf, or never be heard of any more, or a body be found in the Bush and buried by the mounted police, or never found and never buried—what does it matter?

THE DROUGHT TREE

SERIES: LANDSCAPES, 1969
DIMENSIONS: 60.9 x 91.4 CM

The land I love above all others—not because it was kind to me, but because I was born on Australian soil, and because of the foreign father who died at his work in the ranks of Australian pioneers, and because of many things. Australia! my country! her very name is music to me. God bless Australia! for the sake of the great hearts of the heart of her! God keep her clear of the old-world shams and social lies and mockery, and callous commercialism, and sordid shame! and Heaven send that, if ever in my time her sons are called upon to fight for her young life and honour, I die with the first rank of them and be buried in Australian ground.

But this will probably be called false, forced or 'maudlin sentiment' here in England, where the mawkish sentiment of the music halls, and the popular applause it receives, is enough to make a healthy man sick, and is only equalled by music-hall vulgarity. So I'll get on.

In the old digging days the knapsack, or straps-across-the-chest fashion, was tried, but the load pressed on a man's chest and impeded his breathing, and a man needs to have his bellows free on long tracks in hot, stirless weather. Then the 'horse-collar', or rolled military overcoat style—swag over one shoulder and under the other arm—was tried, but it was found to be too hot for the Australian climate, and was discarded along with Wellington boots and leggings. Until recently, Australian city artists and editors—who knew as much about the Bush as Downing Street knows about the British colonies in general—seemed to think the horse-collar was still in existence; and some artists gave the swagman a stick, as if he were a tramp of civilisation with an eye on the backyard and a fear of the dog. English artists, by the way, seem firmly convinced that the Australian Bushman is born in Wellington boots with a polish on 'em you could shave yourself by.

The swag is usually composed of a tent 'fly' or strip of calico (a cover for the swag and a shelter in bad weather—in New Zealand it is oilcloth or waterproof twill), a couple of blankets, blue by custom and preference, as that colour shows the dirt less than any other (hence the name 'bluey' for swag), and the core is composed of spare clothing and small personal effects. To make or 'roll up' your swag: lay the fly or strip of calico on the ground, blueys on top of it, across one end, with eighteen inches or so to spare, lay your spare trousers, shirt, etc., folded, light boots tied together by the laces toe to heel, books, bundle of old letters, portraits, or whatever little knick-knacks you have or care to carry, bag of needles, thread, pen and ink, spare patches for your pants, bootlaces, etc. Lay or arrange the pile so that it will roll evenly with the swag (some pack the lot in an old pillowslip or canvas bag), take a fold over of blanket and calico the whole length on each side, so as to reduce the width of the swag to, say, three feet, throw the spare end, with an inward fold, over the little pile of belongings, and then roll the whole to the other end, using your knees and judgement to make the swag tight, compact and artistic; when within eighteen inches of the loose end take an inward fold in that, and bring it up against the body of the swag. There is a strong suggestion of a roley-poley in a rag about the business, only the ends of the swag are folded in, in rings, and not tied. Fasten the swag with three or four straps, according to judgement and the supply of straps. To the top strap, for the swag is carried (and eased down in shanty bars and against walls or verandah posts when not on the track) in a more or less vertical position—to the top strap, and lowest, or lowest but one, fasten the ends of the shoulder strap (usually a towel is preferred as being softer to the shoulder), your coat being carried outside the swag at the back, under the straps. To the top strap fasten the string of the nose-bag, a calico bag about the size of a pillowslip, containing the tea, sugar and flour bags, bread, meat, baking powder, salt, etc., and brought, when the swag is carried from the left shoulder, over the right onto the chest, and so balancing the swag behind. But a swagman can throw a heavy swag in a nearly vertical position against his spine, slung from one shoulder only and without any balance, and carry it as easily as you might wear your overcoat. Some Bushmen arrange their belongings so neatly and conveniently, with swag straps in a sort of harness, that they can roll up the swag in about a minute, and unbuckle it and throw it out as easily as a roll of wall-paper, and there's the bed ready on the ground with the wardrobe for a pillow. The swag is always used for a seat on the track; it is a soft seat, so trousers last a long time. And, the dust being mostly soft and silky on the long tracks outback, boots last marvellously. Fifteen miles a day is the average with the swag, but you must travel according to the water: if the next bore or tank is five miles on, and the next twenty beyond, you camp at the five-mile water to-night and do the twenty next day. But if it's thirty miles you have to do it. Travelling with the swag in Australia is variously and picturesquely described as 'humping bluey', 'walking Matilda', 'humping Matilda', 'humping your drum', 'being on the wallaby', 'jabbing trotters', and 'tea and sugar burglaring', but most travelling shearers now call themselves trav'lers, and say simply 'on the track', or 'carrying swag'.

And there you have the Australian swag. Men from all the world have carried it—lords and low-class Chinamen, saints and world martyrs, and felons, thieves and murderers, educated gentlemen and boors who couldn't sign their mark, gentlemen who fought for Poland and convicts who fought the world, women, and more than one woman disguised as a man. The Australian swag has held in its core letters and papers in all languages, the honour of great houses, and more than one national secret, papers that would send well-known and highly-respected men to jail, and proofs of the innocence of men going mad in prisons, life tragedies and comedies, fortunes and papers that secured titles and fortunes, and the last pence of lost fortunes, life secrets, portraits of mothers and dead loves, pictures of fair women, heart-breaking old letters written long ago by vanished hands, and the pencilled manuscript of more than one book which will be famous yet.

The weight of the swag varies from the light rouseabout's swag, containing one blanket and a clean shirt, to the 'royal Alfred', with tent and all complete, and weighing part of a ton. Some old sundowners have a mania for gathering, from selectors' and shearers' huts, dust heaps, etc., heart-breaking loads of rubbish which can never be of any possible use to them or anyone else. Here is an inventory of the contents of the swag of an old tramp who was found dead on the track, lying on his face on the sand, with his swag on top of him, and his arms stretched straight out as if he were embracing the Mother Earth, or had made, with his last movement, the Sign of the Cross to the blazing heavens:

Rotten old tent in rags. Filthy blue blanket, patched with squares of red and calico. Half of 'white blanket', nearly black now, patched with pieces of various material and sewn to half of red blanket. Three-bushel sack slit open. Pieces of sacking. Part of a woman's skirt. Two rotten old pairs of moleskin trousers. One leg of a pair of trousers. Back of a shirt. Half a waistcoat. Two tweed coats, green, old and rotting, and patched with calico, blanket, etc. Large bundle of assorted rags for patches, all rotten. Leaky billy can, containing fishing-line, papers, suet, needles and cotton, etc., etc. Jam tins, medicine bottles, corks on strings, to hang on his hat to keep the flies off (a sign of madness in the Bush, for the corks would madden a sane man sooner than the flies could). Three boots of different sizes, all belonging to the right foot, and a left slipper. Coffee-pot, without handle or spout, and quart-pot full of rubbish—broken knives and forks, with the handles burnt off, spoons, etc., etc., picked up on rubbish heaps; and many rusty nails, to be used as buttons, I suppose.

Broken saw blade, hammer, broken crockery, old pannikins, small rusty frying-pan without a handle, children's old shoes, many bits of old boot leather and greenhide, part of yellow-back novel, mutilated English dictionary, grammar and arithmetic book, a ready reckoner, a cookery book, a bulgy Anglo-foreign dictionary, part of a Shakespeare, book in French and book in German, and a book on etiquette and courtship. A heavy pair of blucher boots, with uppers parched and cracked, and soles so patched (patch over patch) with leather, boot protecters, hoop iron and hob nails that they were about two inches thick, and the boots weighed over five pounds. (If you don't believe me go into the Melbourne Museum, where, in a glass case in a place of honour, you will see a similar, perhaps the same, pair of bluchers labelled 'An Example of Colonial Industry'.) And in the core of the swag was a sugar bag tied tightly with a whip-lash, and containing another old skirt, rolled very tight and fastened with many turns of a length of clothesline, which last, I suppose, he carried to hang himself with if he felt that way. The skirt was rolled round a small packet of old portraits and almost undecipherable letters—one from a woman who had evidently been a sensible woman and a widow, and who stated in the letter that she did not intend to get married again as she had enough to do already, slavin' her fingernails off to keep a family, without having a second husband to keep. And her answer was 'final for good and all', and it wasn't no use comin' 'bungfoodlin'' round her again. If he did she'd set Satan onto him. 'Satan' was a dog, I suppose.

The letter was addressed to 'Dear Bill', as were others. There were no envelopes. The letters were addressed from no place in particular, so there weren't any means of identifying the dead man. The police buried him under a gum, and a young trooper cut on the tree the words:

> SACRED TO THE MEMORY OF
> BILL
> WHO DIED.

THE MEN WHO MADE AUSTRALIA

(WRITTEN ON THE OCCASION OF THE
ROYAL VISIT TO AUSTRALIA, 1901)

There'll be royal times in Sydney for the Cuff and Collar Push,
    There'll be lots of dreary drivel and clap-trap
From the men who own Australia, but who never knew the Bush,
    And who could not point their runs out on the map.
Oh, the daily Press will grovel as it never did before,
    There'll be many flags of welcome in the air,
And the Civil Service poet, he shall write odes by the score—
    But the men who made the land will not be there.

You shall meet the awful Lady of the latest Birthday Knight—
    (She is trying to be English, don't-cher-know?)
You shall hear the empty mouthing of the champion blatherskite,
    You shall hear the boss of local drapers blow.
There'll be 'majahs' from the counter, tailors' dummies from the fleet,
    And to represent Australia here to-day,
There's the toady with his card-case and his cab in Downing-street;
    But the men who made Australia—where are they?

Call across the blazing sand wastes of the Never-Never Land!
    There are some who will not answer yet awhile,
Some whose bones rot in the mulga or lie bleaching on the sand,
    Died of thirst to win the land another mile.
Thrown from horses, ripped by cattle, lost on deserts; and the weak,
    Mad through loneliness or drink (no matter which),
Drowned in floods or dead of fever by the sluggish slimy creek—
    These are men who died to make the Wool-Kings rich.

Call across the scrubby ridges where they clear the barren soil,
    And the gaunt Bushwomen share the work of men—
Toil and loneliness for ever—hardship, loneliness and toil—
    Where the brave drought-ruined farmer starts again!
Call across the boundless sheep-runs of a country cursed for sheep—
    Call across the awful scrublands west of Bourke!
But they have no time to listen—they have scarcely time to sleep—
    For the men who conquer deserts have to work.

WITH THE SHEEP

SERIES: WOMEN CONVICTS, 1982
DIMENSIONS: 45.7 x 60.9 CM

Dragged behind the crawling sheep-flock on the hot and dusty plain,
　They must make a cheque to feed the wife and kids—
Riding night-watch round the cattle in the pelting, freezing
　　rain,
　While world-weariness is pressing down the lids.
And away on far out-stations, seldom touched by Heaven's
　　breath,
　In a loneliness that smothers love and hate—
Where they never take white women—there they live the
　　living death
　With a half-caste or a black-gin for a mate.

They must toil to save the gaunt stock in the blazing months
　　of drought,
　When the stinging, blinding blight is in men's eyes—
On the wretched, burnt selections, on the big runs
　　further out
　Where the sand-storm rises lurid to the skies.
Not to profit when the grass is waving waist-high after rain,
　And the mighty clip of wool comes rolling in—
For the Wool-King goes to Paris with his family again
　And the gold that souls are sacrificed to win.

There are carriages in waiting for the swells from over-sea,
　There are banquets in the latest London style,
While the men who made Australia live on damper,
　　junk and tea—
　But the quiet voices whisper, 'Wait a while!'
For the sons of all Australia, they were born to conquer fate—
　And, where charity and friendship are sincere,
Where a sinner is a brother and a stranger is a mate,
　There the future of a nation's written clear.

Aye, the cities claim the triumphs of a land they do not know,
　But all empty is the day they celebrate!
For the men who made Australia federated long ago,
　And the men to rule Australia—they can wait.
Though the bed may be the rough bunk or the gum leaves
　　or the sand,
　And the roof for half the year may be the sky—
There are men amongst the Bushmen who were born
　　to save the land!
　And they'll take their places sternly by-and-by.

There's a whisper on the desert though the sunset breeze
　　hath died
　In the scrubs, though not a breath to stir a bough,
There's a murmur, not of waters, down the Lachlan River side,
　'Tis the spirit of Australia waking now!
There's the weird hymn of the drought-night on the western
　　water-shed,
　Where the beds of unlocked rivers crack and parch;
'Tis the dead that we have buried, and our great unburied dead
　Who are calling now on living men to march!

Round the camp fire of the fencers by the furthest panel west,
　In the men's hut by the muddy billabong,
On the Great North-Western Stock-routes where the drovers
　　never rest,
　They are sorting out the right things from the wrong.
In the shearers' hut the slush lamp shows a haggard,
　　stern-faced man
　Preaching war against the Wool-King to his mates;
And wherever go the billy, water-bag and frying-pan,
　They are drafting future histories of states!

PLOUGHING

SERIES: WOMEN CONVICTS, 1982
DIMENSIONS: 30.4 x 45.7 CM

ONE HUNDRED AND THREE

With the frame of a man, and the face of a boy, and a manner strangely wild,
And the great, wide, wondering, innocent eyes of a silent-suffering child;
With his hideous dress and his heavy boots, he drags to Eternity—
And the Warder says, in a softened tone: 'Keep step, One Hundred and Three.'

'Tis a ghastly travesty of drill—or a ghastly farce of work—
But One Hundred and Three, he catches step with a start, a shuffle and jerk.
'Tis slow starvation in separate cells, and a widow's son is he,
And the widow, she drank before he was born—(Keep step, One Hundred and Three!)

They shut a man in the four-by-eight, with a six-inch slit for air,
Twenty-three hours of the twenty-four, to brood on his virtues there.
And the dead stone walls and the iron door close in as an iron band
On eyes that followed the distant haze far out on the level land.

Bread and water and hominy, and a scrag of meat and a spud,
A Bible and thin flat book of rules, to cool a strong man's blood;
They take the spoon from the cell at night—and a stranger might think it odd;
But a man might sharpen it on the floor, and go to his own Great God.

One Hundred and Three, it is hard to believe that you saddled your horse at dawn;
There were girls that rode through the bush at eve, and girls who lolled on the lawn.
There were picnic parties in sunny bays, and ships on the shining sea;
There were foreign ports in the glorious days—(Hold up, One Hundred and Three!)

A man came out at exercise time from one of the cells to-day:
'Twas the ghastly spectre of one I knew, and I thought he was far away;
We dared not speak, but he signed 'Farewell—fare—well,' and I knew by this
And the number *stamped* on his clothes (not *sewn*) that a heavy sentence was his.

Where five men do the work of a boy, with warders *not* to see,
It is sad and bad and uselessly mad, it is ugly as it can be,
From the flower-beds laid to fit the gaol, in circle and line absurd,
To the gilded weathercock on the church, agape like a strangled bird.

Agape like a strangled bird in the sun, and I wonder what he could see?
The Fleet come in, and the Fleet go out? (Hold up, One Hundred and Three!)
The glorious sea, and the bays and Bush, and the distant mountains blue
(Keep step, keep step, One Hundred and Three, for my lines are halting too).

QUARRYING

SERIES: WOMEN CONVICTS, 1982
DIMENSIONS: 40.6 x 55.8 CM

57

The great, round church with its volume of sound, where we dare not turn our eyes—
They take us there from our separate hells to sing of Paradise.
In all the creeds there is hope and doubt, but of this there is no doubt:
That starving prisoners faint in church, and the warders carry them out.

They double-lock at four o'clock and the warders leave their keys,
And the Governor strolls with a friend at eve through his stone conservatories;
Their window slits are like idiot mouths with square stone chins adrop,
And the weather-stains for the dribble, and the dead flat foreheads atop.

No light save the lights in the yard beneath the clustering lights of the Lord—
And the lights turned in to the window slits of the Observation Ward.
(They eat their meat with their fingers there in a madness starved and dull—
Oh! the padded cells and the 'O—b—s' are nearly always full.)

Rules, regulations—red-tape and rules; all and alike they bind:
Under 'separate treatment' place the deaf; in the dark cell shut the blind!
And somewhere down in his sandstone tomb, with never a word to save,
One Hundred and Three is keeping step, as he'll keep it to his grave.

The press is printing its smug, smug lies, and paying its shameful debt—
It speaks of the comforts that prisoners have, and 'holidays' prisoners get.
The visitors come with their smug, smug smiles through the gaol on a working day,
And the public hears with its large, large ears what authorities have to say.

They lay their fingers on well-hosed walls, and they tread on the polished floor;
They peep in the generous shining cans with their ration Number Four.
And the visitors go with their smug, smug smiles; the reporters' work is done;
Stand up! my men, who have done your time on ration Number One!

Speak up, my men! I was never the man to keep my own bed warm,
I have jogged with you round in the Fools' Parade, and I've worn your uniform;
I've seen you live, and I've seen you die, and I've seen your reason fail—
I've smuggled tobacco and loosened my tongue—and I've been punished in gaol.

Ay! clang the spoon on the iron floor, and shove in the bread with your toe,
And shut with a bang the iron door, and clank the bolt—just so,
With an ignorant oath for a last good-night—or the voice of a filthy thought.
By the Gipsy Blood you have caught a man you'll be sorry that ever you caught.

He shall be buried alive without meat, for a day and a night unheard
If he speak to a fellow prisoner, though he die for want of a word.
He shall be punished, and he shall be starved, and he shall in darkness rot,
He shall be murdered body and soul—and God said, 'Thou shalt not!'

I've seen the remand-yard men go out, by the subway out of the yard—
And I've seen them come in with a foolish grin and a sentence of Three Years Hard.
They send a half-starved man to the court, where the hearts of men they carve—
Then feed him up in the hospital to give him the strength to starve.

You get the gaol-dust in your throat, in your skin the dead gaol-white;
You get the gaol-whine in your voice and in every letter you write.
And in your eyes comes the bright gaol-light—not the glare of the world's distraught,
Not the hunted look, nor the guilty look, but the awful look of the Caught.

There was one I met—'twas a mate of mine—in a gaol that is known to us;
He died—and they said it was 'heart disease'; but he died for want of a truss.
I've knelt at the head of the pallid dead, where the living dead were we,
And I've closed the yielding lids with my thumbs—(Keep step, One Hundred and Three!)

A criminal face is rare in gaol, where all things else are ripe—
It is higher up in the social scale that you'll find the criminal type.
But the kindness of man to man is great when penned in a sandstone pen—
The public call us the 'criminal class', but the warders call us 'the men'.

The brute is a brute, and a kind man kind, and the strong heart does not fail—
A crawler's a crawler everywhere, but a man is a man in gaol!
For forced 'desertion' or drunkenness, or a law's illegal debt,
While never a man who was a man was 'reformed' by punishment yet.

The champagne lady comes home from the course in charge of the criminal swell—
They carry her in from the motor car to the lift in the Grand Hotel.
But armed with the savage Habituals Act they are waiting for you and me,
And the drums, they are beating loud and near. (Keep step, One Hundred and Three!)

The clever scoundrels are all outside, and the moneyless mugs in gaol—
Men do twelve months for a mad wife's lies or Life for a strumpet's tale.
If the people knew what the warders know, and felt as the prisoners feel—
If the people knew, they would storm their gaols as they stormed the old Bastille.

And the cackling, screaming half-human hens who were never mothers nor wives
Would send their sisters to such a hell for the term of their natural lives,
Where laws are made in a Female Fit in the Land of the Crazy Fad,
And drunkards in judgement on drunkards sit and the mad condemn the mad.

The High Church service swells and swells where the tinted Christs look down—
It is easy to see who is weary and faint and weareth the thorny crown.
There are swift-made signs that are not to God, and they march us Hellward then.
It is hard to believe that we knelt as boys to 'for ever and ever, Amen'.

Warders and prisoners are all alike in a dead rot dry and slow—
The author must not write for his own, and the tailor must not sew.
The billet-bound officers dare not speak and discharged men dare not tell
Though many and many an innocent man must brood in this barren hell.

We are most of us criminal, most of us mad, and we do what we can do.
(Remember the Observation Ward and Number Forty-Two.)
There are eyes that see through stone and iron, though the rest of the world be blind
We are prisoners all in God's Great Gaol, but the Governor, He is kind.

They crave for sunlight, they crave for meat, they crave for the might-have-been,
But the cruellest thing in the walls of a gaol is the craving for nicotine.
Yet the spirit of Christ is everywhere where the heart of a man can dwell,
It comes like tobacco in prison—or like news to the separate cell.

They have smuggled him out to the Hospital with no one to tell the tale,
But it's little the doctors and nurses can do for the patient from Starvinghurst Gaol.
He cannot swallow the food they bring, for a gaol-starved man is he,
And the blanket and screen are ready to draw—(Keep step, One Hundred and Three!)

'What were you doing, One Hundred and Three?' and the answer is 'Three years hard,
And a month to go'—and the whisper is low: 'There's the moonlight—out in the yard.'
The drums, they are beating far and low, and the footstep's light and free,
And the angels are whispering over his bed: 'Keep step, One Hundred and Three!'

COMPASSION

SERIES: WOMEN CONVICTS, 1982
DIMENSIONS: 50.8 x 66 CM

DROUGHT-STRICKEN

A dusty patch in the Dingo Scrub,
    That was cleared and ploughed in vain—
(What matters it now if the soil be soaked
    And the bush be dark with rain?)
A heap of stones where the chimney stood,
    And a post on the boundary line—
For forty years of my father's life
    And fifteen years of mine.

It is so hard to make city people understand. If you went out into the dry country now you would wonder not only how sheep or cattle, or even goats, could survive in the drought, but how strong men could live through it. Strong men die often in the heat wave—and what of the women and children out there?

It is a blazing desolation. No sign of crops, no sign of grass, the sods bake white and crumble to dust on the ploughed ground—the surface under the scrub is as bare as a road, and as dusty. Imagine it! nothing but dust and sand and blazing heat for hundreds of miles! All road, all dust. And where is the water? that is one of the first questions that occur to you; for there is no more sign of water than there is of grass. The water is at the 'bore', or in a muddy hole down the creek, or in a dam or tank, with a screen of saplings and boughs over it sometimes, to lessen evaporation. The water is thick and yellow, or the colour of dirty milk, and warm. They have to drink it. And what if the last gallon evaporated, and the next water five, ten, fifteen, or twenty miles away? Well they'd have to take the stock to the water and camp there, or cart it for household purposes on drays in tanks and barrels. And if the nearest water wasn't within reach? what would they do then? God knows!—I don't; but God generally sends a shower at the last moment. What do you know of it, who step a few feet to your tap or filter for a clean, cool drink?

'The country looks awful!' they say, and that expresses it. But you couldn't realise the drought unless you saw it—and then you couldn't realise it unless you lived through it; and even then—well a man does not know what he can go through and leave behind him as an evil dream. The country in the drought is dreadful— it is enough to terrify a new chum; but I heard someone say that men could get used to the infernal regions, and, after going through several droughts, I am inclined to believe it.

THE CARPENTER

SERIES: PLACES AND FACES, 1980
DIMENSIONS: 76.2 x 50.8 CM

It blazes all day—you can see the white heat flowing, dancing, dazzling—and it is stifling all night. Often the smothering hot night is worse than the fiercely glaring day. I had a fancy that one could hear the drought; you've heard the something devilish in the roar of a fire where a fire should not be?—a house on fire—well, it seemed something like that.

Haggard eyes stare vainly at every sign of a cloud for rain. The great white sun rises with almost the heat of noon; and so, day after day, week after week, month after month, until people cease to hope, or even to waste words suggesting that it might rain soon.

'Whenever are we going to get a little rain?' says the baked, gaunt Bushwoman, wearily—and that is all. What do you know of it, you who have not sacrificed the best years of your manhood, the youth of your sons and daughters, and every trace of girlish beauty in your wife's face, trying to make a home in the Bush? What do you know of it, who have not been ruined by the drought time and time again? What do you know of it, who did not depend for a year's provisions on the crop that was scorched from the surface as it sprouted, or the cows and steers that starved to death one by one before your eyes?

And what do the well-meaning good people of the city know of the Bush people who suggest making them objects of charity! If I went into a bare, drought-stricken Bush home to-day, I would glance round and understand it all, but I wouldn't know what to say. I'd be no longer in touch with them—I'd not be suffering with them. I wouldn't attempt to sympathise with them (except perhaps in the case of a quarrel with a neighbouring squatter), for they have no use for sympathy, and the strangeness of it would embarrass them. I'd sit and feel very ill at ease, and I could not meet the Bushwoman's haggard eyes, that look one through and through and size one up; for I'd feel the poor weak citified creature I am. I'd as soon think of striking my father in the face, were he alive, as dream of offering that Bushwoman food and clothes for her family, or putting my hand in my pocket and offering her husband money. If I did so I'd probably be shown the shortest track to the boundary, and so be let down lightly. And, in the evening, they would sit down, in their dusty rags, to their meal of damper and meat, or damper and tea—and brood over a new wrong, an unexpected insult.

No! The Bush people must be helped wholesale—by the Government, by the public, by the people. Every spare penny should be spent on water conservation and irrigation, in sinking tanks and putting down bores, in locking out thousands and thousands of miles of rivers—almost at sea level—where oceans of water waste away after each flood time. To attend to these things is a national work, for the benefit of the whole nation; to neglect them is a national crime—it is suicidal.

The big squatter, bank, or company, with many stations, have a margin for drought losses. There may be rain on one run to make up for the losses through drought on another; and one good season often makes up for several bad ones. It is the small squatter, cockatoo, selector, or farmer who suffers so cruelly, and, in time of drought, they should not be called upon to pay an instalment of one penny an acre on their barren lands. I know how they slave and how they suffer.

I was 'brought up' well 'inside' in 'good country', yet the scrub round our selection was dotted with dusty little patches, with the remains of a fence, a heap of chimney stones, and the ruins of a hut—all that was left of twenty, thirty, forty years of white slavery through blazing droughts.

I like living illustrations. Take our own few neighbours, for instance. There was C——. He alone first, and later on he and his wife—and later on he and his boys and girls—bullocked for years, digging the flinty stumps and trees out of the soil that was almost as flinty, ploughing the hard ground. I've seen some of it blown up with blasting powder before the heavy, strong bullock-plough could make an impression there; trenching it for an orchard and vineyard, and carting every shovelful of manure they could get from the stables of the nearest town. He took fencing and tank-sinking contracts between whiles, and went out with his boys to make flour, meat, tea, and sugar for the family. And they worked like slaves. You don't know how they work in the Bush. The great drought of the early eighties ruined them—the same that burnt us off our selection. The last time I saw old C——he was doing pick-and-shovel work at Prospect—but later on, I believe, he was promoted to the charge of a horse and dray. His old wife was taking in washing in Sydney.

These selections were shoved back in stony, scrubby, barren ridges, while thousands of acres of good land were wanted for sheep, or lying idle as old land grants. But that's another question.

During the same drought W——, the squatter, was driven to the railway line, on his way to a Sydney asylum, handcuffed between two policemen. He was raving mad.

And the B——s. They were the big people there in my time. They had a brick house and a fine vineyard, orchard, and farm. In the old days the old man and his wife worked on stations round, and took up a bit of land and built a humpy there, working nights and Sundays, and begged 'slips' and planted fruit trees. In later years they slaved, men, women, and children, till the eldest daughter looked as old as her mother, and the eldest son was a stoop-shouldered old man at 30.

The old man worked until he died, and the place began to look beautiful. One season they had to scrape the soil away from the roots of every vine of a big new vineyard, and collect the grubs that were destroying the vines; also to treat the fruit trees for a blight. But these are little things in Australian farming. Then, a succession of droughts, and then the dread pleuro pneumonia in the drought. They had fifteen milkers down with it one morning and lost most of them. Then, at last, a terrific hailstorm that stripped the great vineyard of ripening grapes. The eldest son was going to be married that year, 'after wine-making'. He is working for wages on a station now. The rest of the family are scattered, and the bank has taken over the old farm. And so the white slavery of more than half a century of one family, who bullocked at it as only Germans will. The useless sacrifice of the youth, beauty, strength, and happiness of two generations. It is the awful waste of strong, brave lives and long years of toil that appals me.

There was poor Harry S——, our nearest neighbour, on a small selection, who worked like the rest. They were very poor—they often lived and grafted on damper, tea, and sugar. He strained himself lifting logs in a paddock he was clearing. I saw him carried home one day on a sheet of bark, with his face covered. There's a little weazened old woman out there who has been 'queer in her head' ever since her husband was carried home dead. She has bad turns sometimes, and then she keeps crying out: 'Oh, my dear, good, kind husband! He's not dead! He can't be dead! It's a lie they're tellin' me! Oh! why did you tell me such a wicked lie?' and so on, over and over again while the fit lasts.

There was 'Hard R——', the selector, who, one blazing day, when he thought he was alone, fell on his knees behind a stump, out of sight of the house, and prayed for rain as perhaps man never prayed before. But they have little time for praying out there. They must work on holidays and Sundays in the drought, carting water, lifting weak cattle, and dragging them out of mud-holes, cutting down creek-oak and native apple tree for them to eat, burning the carcases, and fighting bush fires. It is backbreaking, heartbreaking work. The young men often rise earliest and work hardest on their wedding days.

There was a woman, a selector's wife, a big, strong, intelligent woman, who had new ideas about farming, and wanted to break away from the old rule-of-thumb system. She had thought out a pretty name for the place when it should be a farm with a brick house, with trees and flowers and vines round it. The ground was about the poorest in the district and the selector carted manure to it. He was a little nuggety Norwegian, an educated man in his country and an intelligent man. He had the reputation of being the honestest and hardest-working man in the district, as well as one of the strongest. He worked round about, carpentering, bricklaying, etc., to make money to keep the family and pay up the instalments on the selections, and to spend on the land; and he cleared it and fenced it, and ploughed it between whiles, and often dug out flinty stumps and 'burnt off' or dug in the dam at night after a long, hard day's work in the nearest town. They used to say he never rested.

One year she persuaded him to save and buy up all the wheaten chaff he could get, and mostly on that she kept the milking cows alive through the terrible drought. Then came that dread cattle disease, and they died one after the other. She doctored them herself while he was away. The eldest son, a delicate boy, was often sick while bleeding the cattle, and she had to do it herself. Several days passed without a fresh case, and she began to hope; several more days, and she rejoiced. Then, in the morning came the children running with the news that there was another cow down—the best milker. Then the woman broke down. She sat on a log, her hands lying hopelessly and helplessly on her knees, and stared—just stared with haggard, hopeless, wide-opened eyes—out over the blazing ruin and desolation that was round the home that was never named. The picture is before me yet— I wish I could paint it. The cows and steers died till all were gone, and there was hot, heavy work to burn the carcases where firewood was scarce.

The selector took another contract, dam-sinking this time, and worked harder than he had ever done before, to make money to buy more cows. But one day he 'felt very queer', and started home to his camp: half-way he felt worse and began to run. He sat down on a stool with his back to the wall of the hut and died.

I saw him when he was dead. The doctor said it was something of the heart and an old thing. Some said it was the only time they ever saw him rest. I thought that the vertical knit in his forehead was deeper than it had been in life, and that he looked as though he were in pain; but they said that that was on account of the post-mortem. And, as I watched—it might have been because of the dry mist that came before my eyes—I fancied that his horny, knotted hands seemed to work as I had seen them work while he slept—as though grasping the handle of an axe or a pick. Death couldn't whiten nor smooth the scarred, knotted fingers, nor mend the twisted, broken nails.

Burials are hurried in the drought. The clay sods on the grave begin to whiten in the fierce heat as the mourners turn away. And, as I turned away from his grave I wished that I could write, or paint, or do something to help these people— my Bush people—for he was my father.

THE UNCULTURED RHYMER
TO HIS CULTURED CRITICS

Fight through ignorance, want, and care—
   Through the griefs that crush the spirit;
Push your way to a fortune fair,
   And the smiles of the world you'll merit.
Long, as a boy, for the chance to learn—
   For the chance that Fate denies you;
Win degrees where the Life-lights burn,
   And scores will teach and advise you.

My cultured friends! you have come too late
   With your bypath nicely graded;
I've fought thus far on my track of Fate,
   And I'll follow the rest unaided.
Must I be stopped by a college gate
   On the track of Life encroaching?
Be dumb to Love, and be dumb to Hate,
   For the lack of a college coaching?

You grope for Truth in a language dead—
   In the dust 'neath tower and steeple!
What know you of the tracks we tread?
   And what know you of our people?
'I must read this, and that, and the rest,'
   And write as the cult expects me?—
I'll read the book that may please me best,
   And write as my heart directs me!

You were quick to pick on a faulty line
   That I strove to put my soul in:
Your eyes were keen for a 'dash' of mine
   In the place of a semi-colon—
And blind to the rest. And is it for such
   As you I must brook restriction?
'I was taught too little?' I learnt too much
   To care for a pedant's diction!

Must I turn aside from my destined way
   For a task your Joss would find me?
I come with strength of the living day,
   And with half the world behind me;
I leave you alone in your cultured halls
   To drivel and croak and cavil:
Till your voice goes further than college walls,
   Keep out of the tracks we travel!

THE CRITIC

Series: Clowns, 1981
Dimensions: 40.6 x 30.4 cm

69

The Drover's Wife

The two-roomed house is built of round timber, slabs, and stringy-bark, and floored with split slabs. A big bark kitchen standing at one end is larger than the house itself, verandah included.

Bush all round—bush with no horizon, for the country is flat. No ranges in the distance. The bush consists of stunted, rotten native apple trees. No undergrowth. Nothing to relieve the eye save the darker green of a few she-oaks which are sighing above the narrow, almost waterless creek. Nineteen miles to the nearest sign of civilization—a shanty on the main road.

The drover, an ex-squatter, is away with sheep. His wife and children are left here alone.

Four ragged, dried-up-looking children are playing about the house. Suddenly one of them yells: 'Snake! Mother, here's a snake!'

The gaunt, sun-browned bushwoman dashes from the kitchen, snatches her baby from the ground, holds it on her left hip, and reaches for a stick.

'Where is it?'

'Here! gone into the wood-heap!' yells the eldest boy—a sharp-faced, excited urchin of eleven. 'Stop there, mother! I'll have him. Stand back! I'll have the beggar!'

'Tommy, come here, or you'll be bit. Come here at once when I tell you, you little wretch!'

The youngster comes reluctantly, carrying a stick bigger than himself. Then he yells, triumphantly:

'There it goes—under the house!' and darts away with club uplifted. At the same time the big, black, yellow-eyed dog-of-all-breeds, who has shown the wildest interest in the proceedings, breaks his chain and rushes after that snake. He is a moment late, however, and his nose reaches the crack in the slabs just as the end of its tail disappears. Almost at the same moment the boy's club comes down and skins the aforesaid nose. Alligator takes small notice of this, and proceeds to undermine the building; but he is subdued after a struggle and chained up. They cannot afford to lose him.

The drover's wife makes the children stand together near the dog-house while she watches for the snake. She gets two small dishes of milk and sets them down near the wall to tempt it to come out; but an hour goes by and it does not show itself.

It is near sunset, and a thunderstorm is coming. The children must be brought inside. She will not take them into the house, for she knows the snake is there, and may at any moment come up through the cracks in the rough slab floor; so she carries several armfuls of firewood into the kitchen, and then takes the children there. The kitchen has no floor—or, rather, an earthen one—called a 'ground floor' in this part of the bush. There is a large, roughly-made table in the centre of the place. She brings the children in, and makes them get on this table. They are two boys and two girls—mere babies. She gives them some supper, and then, before it gets dark, she goes into the house, and snatches up some pillows and bedclothes—expecting to see or lay her hand on the snake any minute. She makes a bed on the kitchen table for the children, and sits down beside it to watch all night.

She has an eye on the corner, and a green sapling club laid in readiness on the dresser by her side, together with her sewing basket and a copy of the *Young Ladies' Journal*. She has brought the dog into the room.

Tommy turns in, under protest, but says he'll lie awake all night and smash that blinded snake.

THE IRISH GIRL

SERIES: PLACES AND FACES, 1980
DIMENSIONS: 60.9 x 45.7 CM

His mother asks him how many times she has told him not to swear.

He has his club with him under the bedclothes, and Jacky protests:

'Mummy! Tommy's skinnin' me alive wif his club. Make him take it out.'

Tommy: 'Shet up, you little—! D'yer want to be bit with the snake?'

Jacky shuts up.

'If yer bit,' says Tommy, after a pause, 'you'll swell up, an' smell, an' turn red an' green an' blue all over till yer burst. Won't he, mother?'

'Now then, don't frighten the child. Go to sleep,' she says.

The two younger children go to sleep, and now and then Jacky complains of being 'skeezed'. More room is made for him. Presently Tommy says: 'Mother! listen to them (adjective) little 'possums. I'd like to screw their blanky necks.'

And Jacky protests drowsily:

'But they don't hurt us, the little blanks!'

Mother: 'There, I told you you'd teach Jacky to swear.' But the remark makes her smile. Jacky goes to sleep.

Presently Tommy asks:

'Mother! Do you think they'll ever extricate the (adjective) kangaroo?'

'Lord! How am I to know, child? Go to sleep.'

'Will you wake me if the snake comes out?'

'Yes. Go to sleep.'

Near midnight. The children are all asleep and she sits there still, sewing and reading by turns. From time to time she glances round the floor and wall-plate, and whenever she hears a noise she reaches for the stick. The thunderstorm comes on, and the wind, rushing through the cracks in the slab wall, threatens to blow out her candle. She places it on a sheltered part of the dresser and fixes up a newspaper to protect it. At every flash of lightning, the cracks between the slabs gleam like polished silver. The thunder rolls, and the rain comes down in torrents.

Alligator lies at full length on the floor, with his eyes turned towards the partition. She knows by this that the snake is there. There are large cracks in that wall opening under the floor of the dwelling-house.

She is not a coward, but recent events have shaken her nerves. A little son of her brother-in-law was lately bitten by a snake, and died. Besides, she has not heard from her husband for six months, and is anxious about him.

He was a drover, and started squatting here when they were married. The drought of 18— ruined him. He had to sacrifice the remnants of his flock and go droving again. He intends to move his family into the nearest town when he comes back, and, in the meantime, his brother, who keeps a shanty on the main road, comes over about once a month with provisions. The wife has still a couple of cows, one horse, and a few sheep. The brother-in-law kills one of the sheep occasionally, gives her what she needs of it, and takes the rest in return for other provisions.

She is used to being left alone. She once lived like this for eighteen months. As a girl she built the usual castles in the air; but all her girlish hopes and aspirations have long been dead. She finds all the excitement and recreation she needs in the *Young Ladies' Journal*, and, Heaven help her! takes a pleasure in the fashion-plates.

Her husband is an Australian, and so is she. He is careless, but a good enough husband. If he had the means he would take her to the city and keep her there like a princess. They are used to being apart, or at least she is. 'No use fretting,' she says. He may forget sometimes that he is married; but if he has a good cheque when he comes back he will give most of it to her. When he had money he took her to the city several times—hired a railway sleeping compartment, and put up at the best hotels. He also bought her a buggy, but they had to sacrifice that along with the rest.

The last two children were born in the bush—one while her husband was bringing a drunken doctor, by force, to attend to her. She was alone on this occasion, and very weak. She had been ill with a fever. She prayed to God to send her assistance. God sent Black Mary—the 'whitest' gin in all the land. Or, at least, God sent 'King Jimmy' first, and he sent Black Mary. He put his black face round the door-post, took in the situation at a glance, and said cheerfully: 'All right, Missis—I bring my old woman, she down alonga creek.'

One of her children died while she was here alone. She rode nineteen miles for assistance, carrying the dead child.

It must be near one or two o'clock. The fire is burning low. Alligator lies with his head resting on his paws, and watches the wall. He is not a very beautiful dog to look at, and the light shows numerous old wounds where the hair will not grow. He is afraid of nothing on the face of the earth or under it. He will tackle a bullock as readily as he will tackle a flea. He hates all other dogs—except kangaroo-dogs—and has a marked dislike to friends or relations of the family. They seldom call, however. He sometimes makes friends with strangers. He hates snakes and has killed many, but he will be bitten some day and die; most snake-dogs end that way.

Now and then the bushwoman lays down her work and watches, and listens, and thinks. She thinks of things in her own life, for there is little else to think about.

The rain will make the grass grow, and this reminds her how she fought a bush fire once while her husband was away. The grass was long, and very dry, and the fire threatened to burn her out. She put on an old pair of her husband's trousers and beat out the flames with a green bough, till great drops of sooty perspiration stood out on her forehead and ran in streaks down her blackened arms. The sight of his mother in trousers greatly amused Tommy, who worked like a little hero by her side, but the terrified baby howled lustily for his 'mummy'. The fire would have mastered her but for four excited bushmen who arrived in the nick of time. It was a mixed-up affair all round; when she went to take up the baby he screamed and struggled convulsively, thinking it was a 'black man', and Alligator, trusting more to the child's sense than his own instinct, charged furiously, and (being old and slightly deaf) did not in his excitement at first recognize his mistress's voice, but continued to hang on to the moleskins until choked off by Tommy with a saddle-strap. The dog's sorrow for his blunder, and his anxiety to let it be known that it was all a mistake, was as evident as his ragged tail and a twelve-inch grin could make it. It was a glorious time for the boys; a day to look back to, and talk about, and laugh over for many years.

She thinks how she fought a flood during her husband's absence. She stood for hours in the drenching downpour, and dug an overflow gutter to save the dam across the creek. But she could not save it. There are things that a bushwoman cannot do. Next morning the dam was broken, and her heart was nearly broken too, for she thought how her husband would feel when he came home and saw the result of years of labour swept away. She cried then.

She also fought the *pleuro-pneumonia*—dosed and bled the few remaining cattle, and wept again when her two best cows died.

Again, she fought a mad bullock that besieged the house for a day. She made bullets and fired at him through cracks in the slabs with an old shotgun. He was dead in the morning. She skinned him and got seventeen-and-six for the hide.

She also fights the crows and eagles that have designs on her chickens. Her plan of campaign is very original. The children cry 'Crows, mother!' and she rushes out and aims a broomstick at the birds as though it were a gun, and says, 'Bung!' The crows leave in a hurry; they are cunning, but a woman's cunning is greater.

Occasionally a bushman in the horrors, or a villainous-looking sundowner, comes and nearly scares the life out of her. She generally tells the suspicious-looking stranger that her husband and two sons are at work below the dam, or over at the yard, for he always cunningly enquires for the boss.

Only last week a gallows-faced swagman—having satisfied himself that there were no men on the place—threw his swag down on the verandah, and demanded tucker. She gave him something to eat; then he expressed his intention of staying for the night. It was sundown then. She got a batten from the sofa, loosened the dog, and confronted the stranger, holding the batten in one hand and the dog's collar with the other. 'Now you go!' she said. He looked at her and at the dog, said 'All right, mum,' in a cringing tone, and left. She was a determined-looking woman, and Alligator's yellow eyes glared unpleasantly—besides, the dog's chewing-up apparatus greatly resembled that of the reptile he was named after.

She has few pleasures to think of as she sits here alone by the fire, on guard against a snake. All days are much the same to her; but on Sunday afternoon she dresses herself, tidies the children, smartens up baby, and goes for a lonely walk along the bush-track, pushing an old perambulator in front of her. She does this every Sunday. She takes as much care to make herself and the children look smart as she would if she were going to do the block in the city. There is nothing to see, however, and not a soul to meet. You might walk for twenty miles along this track without being able to fix a point in your mind, unless you are a bushman. This is because of the everlasting, maddening sameness of the stunted trees—that monotony which makes a man long to break away and travel as far as trains can go, and sail as far as ships can sail—and further.

But this bushwoman is used to the loneliness of it. As a girl-wife she hated it, but now she would feel strange away from it.

She is glad when her husband returns, but does not gush or make a fuss about it. She gets him something good to eat, and tidies up the children.

She seems contented with her lot. She loves her children, but has no time to show it. She seems harsh to them. Her surroundings are not favourable to the development of the 'womanly' or sentimental side of nature.

It must be near morning now; but the clock is in the dwelling-house. Her candle is nearly done; she forgot that she was out of candles. Some more wood must be got to keep the fire up, and so she shuts the dog inside and hurries round to the wood-heap. The rain has cleared off. She seizes a stick, pulls it out, and—crash! the whole pile collapses.

Yesterday she bargained with a stray blackfellow to bring her some wood, and while he was at work she went in search of a missing cow. She was absent an hour or so, and the native black made good use of his time. On her return she was so astonished to see a good heap of wood by the chimney, that she gave him an extra fig of tobacco, and praised him for not being lazy. He thanked her, and left with head erect and chest well out. He was the last of his tribe and a King; but he had built that wood-heap hollow.

She is hurt now, and tears spring to her eyes as she sits down again by the table. She takes a handkerchief to wipe the tears away, but pokes her eyes with her bare fingers instead. The handkerchief is full of holes, and she finds that she has put her thumb through one, and her forefinger through another.

This makes her laugh, to the surprise of the dog. She has a keen, very keen, sense of the ridiculous; and some time or other she will amuse bushmen with the story.

She has been amused before like that. One day she sat down 'to have a good cry', as she said—and the old cat rubbed against her dress and 'cried too'. Then she had to laugh.

It must be near daylight. The room is very close and hot because of the fire. Alligator still watches the wall from time to time. Suddenly he becomes greatly interested; he draws himself a few inches nearer the partition, and a thrill runs through his body. The hair on the back of his neck begins to bristle, and the battle-light is in his yellow eyes. She knows what this means, and lays her hand on the stick. The lower end of one of the partition slabs has a large crack on both sides. An evil pair of small, bright bead-like eyes glisten at one of these holes. The snake—a black one—comes slowly out, about a foot, and moves its head up and down. The dog lies still, and the woman sits as one fascinated. The snake comes out a foot further. She lifts her stick, and the reptile, as though suddenly aware of danger, sticks his head in through the crack on the other side of the slab, and hurries to get his tail round after him. Alligator springs, and his jaws come together with a snap. He misses, for his nose is large and the snake's body closes down in the angle formed by the slabs and the floor. He snaps again as the tail comes round. He has the snake now, and tugs it out eighteen inches. Thud, thud comes the woman's club on the ground. Alligator pulls again. Thud, thud. Alligator gives another pull and he has the snake out—a black brute, five feet long. The head rises to dart about, but the dog has the enemy close to the neck. He is a big, heavy dog, but quick as a terrier. He shakes the snake as though he felt the original curse in common with mankind. The eldest boy wakes up, seizes his stick, and tries to get out of bed, but his mother forces him back with a grip of iron. Thud, thud—the snake's back is broken in several places. Thud, thud—its head is crushed, and Alligator's nose skinned again.

She lifts the mangled reptile on the point of her stick, carries it to the fire, and throws it in; then piles on the wood, and watches the snake burn. The boy and dog watch, too. She lays her hand on the dog's head, and all the fierce, angry light dies out of his yellow eyes. The younger children are quieted, and presently go to sleep. The dirty-legged boy stands for a moment in his shirt, watching the fire. Presently he looks up at her, sees the tears in her eyes, and, throwing his arms round her neck, exclaims:

'Mother, I won't never go drovin'; blast me if I do!'

And she hugs him to her worn-out breast and kisses him; and they sit thus together while the sickly daylight breaks over the bush.

Past Carin'

Now up and down the siding brown
  The great black crows are flyin',
And down below the spur, I know,
  Another 'milker's' dyin';
The crops have withered from the ground,
  The tank's clay bed is glarin',
But from my heart no tear nor sound,
  For I have gone past carin'—
  Past worryin' or carin',
  Past feelin' aught or carin';
  But from my heart no tear nor sound,
  For I have gone past carin'.

Through Death and Trouble, turn about,
  Through hopeless desolation,
Through flood and fever, fire and drought,
  And slavery and starvation;
Through childbirth, sickness, hurt, and blight,
  And nervousness an' scarin',
Through bein' left alone at night,
  I've got to be past carin'.
  Past botherin' or carin',
  Past feelin' and past carin';
  Through city cheats and neighbours' spite,
  I've come to be past carin'.

Our first child took, in days like these,
  A cruel week in dyin',
All day upon her father's knees,
  Or on my poor breast lyin';
The tears we shed—the prayers we said
  Were awful, wild—despairin'!
I've pulled three through, and buried two
  Since then—and I'm past carin'.
  I've grown to be past carin',
  Past worryin' and wearin';
  I've pulled three through and buried two
  Since then, and I'm past carin'.

'Twas ten years first, then came the worst,
  All for a dusty clearin',
I thought, I thought my heart would burst
  When first my man went shearin';
He's drovin' in the great North-west,
  I don't know how he's farin';
For I, the one that loved him best,
  Have grown to be past carin'.
  I've grown to be past carin'.
  Past lookin' for or carin';
  The girl that waited long ago,
  Has lived to be past carin'.

My eyes are dry, I cannot cry,
  I've got no heart for breakin',
But where it was in days gone by,
  A dull and empty achin'.
My last boy ran away from me,
  I know my temper's wearin',
But now I only wish to be
  Beyond all signs of carin'.
  Past wearyin' or carin',
  Past feelin' and despairin';
  And now I only wish to be
  Beyond all signs of carin'.

THE MATRIARCH

SERIES: THE AUSTRALIANS, 1978
DIMENSIONS: 60.9 x 50.8 CM

FACES IN THE STREET

They lie, the men who tell us in a loud decisive tone
That want is here a stranger, and that misery's unknown;
For where the nearest suburb and the city proper meet
My window-sill is level with the faces in the street—
    Drifting past, drifting past,
    To the beat of weary feet—
While I sorrow for the owners of those faces in the street.

And cause I have to sorrow, in a land so young and fair,
To see upon those faces stamped the marks of Want and Care;
I look in vain for traces of the fresh and fair and sweet
In sallow, sunken faces that are drifting through the street—
    Drifting on, drifting on,
    To the scrape of restless feet;
I can sorrow for the owners of the faces in the street.

In hours before the dawning dims the starlight in the sky
The wan and weary faces first begin to trickle by,
Increasing as the moments hurry on with morning feet,
Till like a pallid river flow the faces in the street—
    Flowing in, flowing in,
    To the beat of hurried feet—
Ah! I sorrow for the owners of those faces in the street.

The human river dwindles when 'tis past the hour of eight,
Its waves go flowing faster in the fear of being late;
But slowly drag the moments, whilst beneath the dust and heat
The city grinds the owners of the faces in the street—
    Grinding body, grinding soul,
    Yielding scarce enough to eat—
Oh! I sorrow for the owners of the faces in the street.

THE DRAMATIST

SERIES: THE AUSTRALIANS, 1978
DIMENSIONS: 76.2 x 55.8 CM

And then the only faces till the sun is sinking down
Are those of outside toilers and the idlers of the town,
Save here and there a face that seems a stranger in the street
Tells of the city's unemployed upon his weary beat—
   Drifting round, drifting round,
   To the tread of listless feet—
Ah! my heart aches for the owner of that sad face in the street.

And when the hours on lagging feet have slowly dragged away,
And sickly yellow gaslights rise to mock the going day,
Then flowing past my window like a tide in its retreat,
Again I see the pallid stream of faces in the street—
   Ebbing out, ebbing out,
   To the drag of tired feet,
While my heart is aching dumbly for the faces in the street.

And now all blurred and smirched with vice the day's sad pages end,
For while the short 'large hours' towards the longer 'small hours' trend,
With smiles that mock the wearer, and with words that half entreat,
Delilah pleads for custom at the corner of the street—
   Sinking down, sinking down,
   Battered wreck by tempests beat—
A dreadful, thankless trade is hers, that Woman of the Street.

But, ah! to dreader things than these our fair young city comes,
For in its hearts are growing thick the filthy dens and slums,
Where human forms shall rot away in sites for swine unmeet,
And ghostly faces shall be seen unfit for any street—
   Rotting out, rotting out,
   For the lack of air and meat—
In dens of vice and horror that are hidden from the street.

I wonder would the apathy of wealthy men endure
Were all their windows level with the faces of the Poor?
Ah! Mammon's slaves, your knees shall knock, your hearts in terror beat,
When God demands a reason for the sorrows of the street,
   The wrong things and the bad things
   And the sad things that we meet
In the filthy lane and alley, and the cruel, heartless street.

I left the dreadful corner where the steps are never still,
And sought another window overlooking gorge and hill;
But when the night came dreary with the driving rain and sleet,
They haunted me—the shadows of those faces in the street,
    Flitting by, flitting by,
    Flitting by with noiseless feet,
And with cheeks but little paler than the real ones in the street.

Once I cried: 'Oh, God Almighty! if Thy might doth still endure,
Now show me in a vision for the wrongs of Earth a cure.'
And, lo! with shops all shuttered I beheld a city's street,
And in the warning distance heard the tramp of many feet,
    Coming near, coming near,
    To a drum's dull distant beat,
And soon I saw the army that was marching down the street.

Then, like a swollen river that has broken bank and wall,
The human flood came pouring with the red flags over all,
And kindled eyes all blazing bright with revolution's heat,
And flashing swords reflecting rigid faces in the street.
    Pouring on, pouring on.
    To a drum's loud threatening beat,
And the war-hymns and the cheering of the people in the street.

And so it must be while the world goes rolling round its course,
The warning pen shall write in vain, the warning voice grow hoarse,
But not until a city feels Red Revolution's feet
Shall its sad people miss awhile the terrors of the street—
    The dreadful everlasting strife
    For scarcely clothes and meat
In that pent tack of living death—the city's cruel street.

BARTA

Wide solemn eyes that question me,
   Wee hand that pats my head—
Where only two have stroked before,
   And both of them are dead.
'Ah, poo-ah Daddy mine,' she says,
   With wondrous sympathy—
Oh, baby girl, you don't know how
   You break the heart in me!

Let friends and kinsfolk work their worst,
   And the world say what it will,
Your baby arms go round my neck—
   I'm your own Daddy still!
And you kiss me and I kiss you,
   Fresh kisses frank and free—
Ah, baby girl, you don't know how
   You break the heart in me!

I dreamed when I was good that when
   The snow showed in my hair,
A household angel in her teens
   Would flit about my chair,
To comfort me as I grew old;
   But that shall never be—
Ah, baby girl, you don't know how
   You break the heart in me!

But one shall love me while I live
   And soothe my troubled head,
And never hear an unkind word
   Of me when I am dead.
Her eyes shall light to hear my name
   Howe'er disgraced it be—
Ah, baby girl, you don't know how
   You help the heart in me!

GIRL WITH MANDOLIN

SERIES: THE AUSTRALIANS, 1978
DIMENSIONS: 55.8 x 40.6 CM